The Gathering Storm

Glasgow-born Lynne McEwan is a former newspaper photographer turned crime author. She's covered stories including the Fall of the Berlin Wall and the first Gulf War in addition to many high profile murder cases. She currently lives in Lincoln and is in the final year of an MA in Crime Fiction at the University of East Anglia.

Also by Lynne McEwan

Detective Shona Oliver

turned the lifeboat's bow towards her, Shona knew this would be their last attempt to establish a tow.

Some benevolent force must have been looking down on them. For a few seconds the waves eased. Callum threw the line. Shona grabbed it and in one fluid movement made it fast around the cleat bolted to the yacht's foredeck. Moments later, the lifeboat turned and began to pull the three-ton deadweight of the yacht out of the surf.

But the pause was only the storm drawing breath. The wind had risen to force 6 and the tide's grip strengthened. The sea was playing like a cat, batting them around with its giant paws. It was clear the *Margaret Wilson* couldn't do this alone. Shona saw Callum on the radio. Next minute, he was leaning forward, shouting to her.

'Silloth are on their way.' He gave her a thumbs up. The *John Shenton*, a larger B-class Atlantic 85, was among the fastest in the fleet, but the conditions would limit their speed.

For the next fifteen minutes, the *Margaret Wilson* hung on in a tug of war between lifeboat and tide, while Shona stayed at her position on the bow of the *Ranger*. For long moments, she lost sight of the lifeboat in the deep troughs between the mounds of water, as if far out to sea, without another soul in sight: alone, save for the silent Manxman. Even the birds, great flocks of migrating whooper swans, pink-footed geese and their barnacle cousins normally so common on the Solway, had fled the storm.

Continuing to hang on tight, Shona turned once more to check on the yachtsman, his ragdoll form lashed to a safety line and slumped in the cockpit. At the same moment, she heard a sharp crack, and something whipped through the air close to her. Shona gasped as she was propelled backwards against the metal stanchion, pain running through her ribs like an electric shock. The towline had snapped.

Freed from her tether, and only metres from the Drumroof Bank, the *Ramsey Ranger* spun in a panicked circle. Below the bow, the sea was more sand than water, a brown broth kicked up by the yacht's keel dragging across the bottom. A thick rasping vibration shook the hull before she wrenched free again, but the vessel was listing badly, pumps clogged with sand. The weight of wind on her rigging was prising loose halyards and the stays that held the mast in place. Steel wires flayed the deck, a shrill counterpoint to the roar of the storm.

'Larry, Larry!' she shouted. 'Get below!'

Tommy fought to control the lifeboat, as Callum reeled in his end of the broken rope and prepared to throw another towline.

The Manxman didn't move. Shona cursed, then edged back along the angled deck, boots braced against the submerged gunwale as the sea grasped hungrily at her legs. Larry was slumped in the cabin doorway, his skin waxy, eyes closed.

She shook him.

'Look at me, Larry,' she shouted, wincing at the stabbing pain in her side. It was obvious he was shutting down as hypothermia set in. 'Stay awake. You need to go below.'

'No, no,' he said, trying to push her away.

Was he afraid he'd be trapped if the boat sank? She could understand that, but if he thought that by remaining on deck he could scramble onto Drumroof Bank, he was mistaken. Though it dried at low water, this only revealed a scored surface littered with shipwrecks. If they attempted to leave the yacht, they'd be washed away by the powerful waves or sucked down where the sea burrowed below, creating lethal, shifting quicksand.

Leaning over him, she stuck her head through the cabin doorway.

'No, you can't go down there,' Larry shouted.

Another bolt of pain shot through Shona's ribs as he tried to block her. She grimaced.

'It's dry, Larry. Look at me.' She grabbed the front of his lifejacket. 'Get into the cabin now.' Without further ceremony she bundled him feet-first down the companionway. He turned and clung to the steps, blocking her from following and himself from sliding further into the cabin.

She needed to secure the whipping wires to the mast and get back to the foredeck, re-establish the tow.

But he grabbed at her lifejacket. 'You shouldn't be here.'

She was drained. A deep throbbing pain had set in, just below her shoulder blade, worsening with every breath. Her hands and face were numb with cold. They'd been battling the conditions for nearly an hour. The adrenaline was wearing off. She thought of Becca finding her mother's note and looking out from the long windows of High Pines at the worsening weather.

'I won't leave you,' Shona said. 'We won't leave you, Larry. Just hang on. We'll make it.'

And when she looked up again, she knew she was right. The orange bulk of the *John Shenton* was there, battling against the headwind. The cavalry had arrived. With a final effort, Shona caught the new towline. The *Ramsey Ranger* would be saved and, at last, they'd all be going home.

Chapter 3

The next morning, Shona drew back her bedroom curtains, wincing at the pain in her side. Below, in the estuary, the *Ramsey Ranger* was tethered to a mooring buoy. The yacht was battered but in one piece, rather like herself. Tommy had declined to take on the vessel's repairs, claiming he was too busy. Shona knew that wasn't true. January was quiet in the boatyard, with few visiting vessels and the local pleasure craft mothballed for the winter.

When Shona queried the decision, Tommy had responded that Larry was a Manxman, and they had quite a history of raiding all along this coast. Since the burning of Kirkcudbright was five hundred years ago, Shona thought it was a long time to bear a grudge, but she supposed it was Tommy's choice. He was probably worried he wouldn't get paid for the work, and the debt would be difficult to recover from the self-governing Isle of Man.

Her Arts and Crafts dressing table sat next to the broad sweep of the window. She'd bought it at Camden Market, not far from their former home in London, a large Victorian terrace. Here, it was the only antique piece in the thoroughly modern bedroom, a throwback to other times, other imagined futures. In the foxed mirror, she studied the bruise on her left cheekbone spreading up to her brow, then added another layer of foundation.

Yesterday's lifeboat shout had been tough but worthwhile. The final tally was badly bruised ribs for Shona, and lumps and bumps all round for her crewmates, set against a life saved. Larry Smith the Manxman remained a positive statistic for the RNLI and had avoided becoming a negative one for Police Scotland's sudden-deaths tally.

She made a final check on her handywork in the mirror, keeping her attention from the king-sized bed behind her. In the last few months, she'd often told herself that Rob was just in another room, or out on an errand. All she had to do was keep going and one day soon, when she looked up, he'd be there again. Rob had been sentenced to ten years, due to the high value of the laundering operation. Now, without his presence at home, she was experiencing a new vulnerability.

Her job regularly exposed her to the worst of humanity. Every bad thing you could imagine was somewhere in a case file. But it ran deeper than that. She'd realised they were like the couple in the old-fashioned weather clock that had hung in the hallway of her grandmother's tenement flat. On fine days, a smiling man would appear in shirtsleeves from the little Alpine chalet. When rain was forecast, which was most of the time in Glasgow, a woman bearing an umbrella took his place. Rob's perpetual sunshine – his refusal to acknowledge problems – often irritated Shona, but now she found she missed it. Perhaps that was the strength of their marriage. They each mitigated a little of the other's extreme weather, allowing neither pattern to become fixed.

Taking her navy suit jacket from its hanger, she headed downstairs, one step at a time, hand on the pale beechwood banister. Shona sometimes credited the tower-like

High Pines' sixty-six steps with keeping her fit. Pre-coffee and painkillers, she could have done without the workout.

The house was wedged into the hillside, among a clump of trees from which it took its name. On the south-west side, above a steep, terraced garden, High Pines rose four floors high, fronted by deep bay windows giving it a glorious view of the estuary and the Solway Riviera's spectacular sunsets. The top floor contained a lounge. Below were the family bedrooms, then a further kitchen, utility and dining level. On the lowest floor were guest rooms, each with its own private terrace from which steps led down through the garden, past a studio where Becca often did her homework projects, directly to the shore. At the rear of the house stood a double garage and a large, gated parking area, the steep hillside bringing it level with the back door into the utility room.

Becca was in the kitchen, hunched in an oversized fleece and leggings, trainers braced against the edge of the kitchen table as she studied her phone. She had her mother's colouring and heart-shaped face but had long surpassed her in height, adding a pierced nose stud along the way. She took in Shona's smart trousers and pale lemon blouse.

'You're not going into work?'

'Just a meeting.'

Detective Superintendent Clive Davies had messaged Shona last night. A face-to-face welfare chat was how he'd described it. To Shona, such a meeting sounded ominous, but she wasn't about to share that with her daughter.

'What's your plan for today?' Shona said, keen to move the conversation forward. 'Feet off the table, please.'

She flicked the kettle switch. They were out of real coffee. Instant would have to do.

'The doctor said you had to rest, 'cause of your ribs,' Becca said, undeterred. She slid her trainers to the floor and sprang up. Taking a bowl from the draining board, she began filling it with muesli. Becca pointed her index finger at her mother, then at the seat she'd just vacated. 'Sit.'

In the absence of her father, Becca had stepped into his role of cook and all-round domestic fixer, but delivered with a liberal dose of her mother's directness. Shona felt an upswell of love for her sixteen-year-old daughter, a pain in her chest that had nothing to do with her bruised ribs. Their sometimes difficult relationship had morphed into one where, although they weren't always in agreement, at least they had each other's backs.

'I'm getting some Insta reels together,' Becca said, putting a mug of black coffee and the bowl of muesli in front of her mother. 'Try to drum up some customers for us.'

Shona didn't have any social media accounts beyond an ancient and defunct Facebook page, so the High Pines Instagram account had defaulted to her daughter. Shona's impression was that it had mostly been Becca's enterprise anyway.

'I don't want you neglecting your schoolwork.' Shona took a sip of coffee. Becca was studying four Scottish Highers online. The home-schooling that had brought her ten good International GCSE qualifications last year had been Rob's domain. Shona had noted the number of study hours required for the courses. 'You need to set out an action plan and review your progress every day. Keep up with all your subjects.' As far as Shona could make out, the bulk of Becca's time went on her Environmental Science and History Highers, with less enthusiasm for English and Maths. 'Upload the book essay you're working on to Google Docs and share the file with me. We can chat about it later.'

'If you were here, we could chat about it now.'

'You know I have to work,' Shona said, eyebrows raised in a warning expression to Becca to moderate her tone.

'You have to rest,' Becca shot back.

When Tommy'd heard her diagnosis, he'd banned Shona from the boat crew for two weeks, but the doctor has stopped short of ordering her off work. Possible complications were breathlessness, chest infections and coughing that might lead to a stress fracture or rupture of the rib cartilage. She'd assured the medic she'd take it easy. Office duties only.

'I'll be back this afternoon,' Shona said. 'I need to see that the business isn't taking over your life.'

There were no guests at present. Without Rob, the bed and breakfast hadn't been sustainable, so they'd converted the two en-suite guest rooms to self-catering studio lets, each with mini fridge, microwave and kettle in the small lounge areas. It had been hard work, and Shona had been grateful for it, throwing herself into the minutiae of domestic and B&B reorganisation with the zeal she normally reserved for serious crimes. In snatched moments, boxes of Rob's financial records had been pulled from the garage. As a City of London cop, she'd dealt with economic and so-called 'white-collar' crimes, so she had begun reviewing the evidence and unpicking exactly how Rob had found himself jailed. The key to Delfont's involvement was in the financial documents somewhere, she was sure of it, though perhaps you'd only see it if you were looking for it.

In the meantime, there were still B&B bookings to process, cleaning and bed changes to be done. Shona's injury might mean more of that physical work would fall to Becca. They couldn't afford to employ anyone. Profit margins, always small, had shrunk further. Her Police Scotland salary was all that was keeping them afloat.

Becca opened her mouth to argue that her mother should stay at home but closed it again at Shona's expression.

'I will rest,' Shona assured her. 'Tonight. And you can show me what you've been doing.'

Shona finished her muesli, making an effort to move as naturally as possible knowing her daughter's beady eye was on her, then scrolled through her phone messages. She'd call Dumfries CID, check with her sergeant, Murdo O'Halloran, that nothing had come in since she'd updated him on her plans last night. A second coffee and two painkillers later, she was about to dial his number when she heard footsteps in the utility room. DC Ravi Sarwar stuck his head around the kitchen door and flashed them both his megawatt smile.

'Morning, boss.'

Glasgow had an undeniable reputation for football and drinking but there was a third obsession – fashion. Ravi, a native Weegie, rarely disappointed in the style stakes. This morning, he was dressed in slim jeans and a forest green puffer jacket over a teal cashmere sweater. At thirty, he retained the coltish frame of a younger man. Shona had seen him dodge a punch, then return it with surprising accuracy and power, although his charm and quiet authority rarely made that necessary.

Shona looked at Becca. 'Did you call him?'

'Did the doctor say you could drive?' Becca shot back.

'He didn't say I couldn't,' Shona retorted. That wasn't entirely true. The injured ribs were on her left side, and the doctor had said that might make changing gears difficult. 'Excruciating' was the actual word he'd used.

'It's no bother,' Ravi interjected, ever the peacemaker. 'When Murdo said you were heading up to Kilmarnock, I thought we could pool resources. There's some folk I need to see and, to be honest, I could do with picking your brains on a few things. I've been asked for input on the new Equality, Diversity and Inclusion Strategy. I've got a handle on the racism and bullying, but the misogyny is doing ma head in.'

'Aye, it does that,' Shona said drily.

'And Ravi knows about your ribs, 'cause I texted Martin about some maths stuff last night,' Becca said, clearing away her mother's dishes. 'It's not a state secret, is it?'

Ravi and his partner, Martin, an addiction counsellor, had become a sensible and supportive influence in Becca's life, although Shona was aware they'd promised they'd take her clubbing in Glasgow – *for the party of your life* – the minute she turned eighteen. They'd have to see about that.

Looking from Becca to Ravi, she knew she was outnumbered. In truth, she wasn't looking forward to the ninety-minute drive to the Divisional HQ. 'Fine. If it keeps everyone happy. Let's go.'

Chapter 4

Shona eased herself into the passenger seat of the Audi. She glanced at her watch. She found herself doing that more and more these days. Time had sped up. She could do without this excursion.

After Shona and Ravi had unpicked the key points and objectives needed for the report, they fell into an easy silence, Ravi's chilled-out playlist filling the car as he took the curves smoothly. They left the Solway behind and climbed through the Galloway hills, and Shona's mind began to drift to the coming interview.

Ever since Rob's sentencing, she'd been sure Detective Superintendent Davies wanted to sideline her. So far, there'd been minimal media fallout. *Police Scotland does not comment on investigations undertaken by other constabularies or officers' personal matters* was the bulwark against which all official enquiries had stalled. It had helped that she was part of the lifeboat family and none of her friends or neighbours in Kirkness could be persuaded to talk to the press. But if she was assigned as SIO on a big case, the fact her husband had gone to jail for money laundering would reignite interest and become an unnecessary distraction. In Davies's position, she might have considered removing her a prudent course of action.

The fear of what Rob's conviction would mean for the upcoming rape and sexual assault trial of DCI Harry

Delfont – her former boss – surfaced once more in Shona's mind and she felt the familiar stomach-churning anxiety. The evidence against Delfont was strong but the conviction rate for rape pitifully small. He had filmed himself abusing apparently unconscious women, including Shona. Two other victims had been identified as fellow police officers, but he'd claimed it was consensual sex games. Rob's misdeeds were now a matter of public record. All Delfont's defence had to do was discredit her by association. Was the whole allegation an attempt by Shona to blackmail her boss, a senior City cop, to save her husband from prosecution? The defence didn't even need to say it out loud, they just had to encourage the jury to wonder. The injustice made her want to howl with rage.

All Shona recalled of the incident was waking up in her car on the hard shoulder of the Docklands Expressway with a traffic cop tapping at her window. She couldn't remember leaving the office party at which she was convinced her single glass of wine had been spiked. Once at the police station, she discovered her underwear was on back to front. It was only much later, when the investigating officers, brought in from the neighbouring Metropolitan Police, had shown her the video that she'd understood with a sick horror what Delfont had done to her. In the intervening period, he'd given her a choice – face a drink-driving charge that would see her dismissed from the force or move elsewhere. Jump, before she was pushed. Rob had been made redundant; Becca was in trouble at school. She'd had to protect her family, so she'd jumped. The thought of how successfully he'd manipulated her made her head pound, pain radiating upwards through her temples as she gritted her teeth.

Delfont must be found guilty, if she was ever going to free Rob. It was the tipping point that would bring her former boss's whole corrupt edifice tumbling down. Other victims would be emboldened by the prospect of justice and come forward, and the resultant professional standards inquiry would surely find his links to organised crime, especially if she uncovered evidence in Rob's papers. But if Delfont was acquitted – and juries were fickle, as Rob knew to his cost – she'd be the lying, vindictive, hysterical, corrupt officer. Any one of those adjectives would finish her career. Her knuckles were white, gripping the Audi's passenger seat, her breath coming fast and shallow. She became aware of Ravi easing off the gas and throwing sideways glances at her.

'You all right, boss?'

'Yes,' she snapped, then regretted venting her rage on her DC. 'Ribs,' she offered by way of explanation.

'Want me to pull over?'

'No, no. You're fine. Let's just get there.'

Shona spent the rest of the journey with her face turned towards the passenger window and Ravi had the sense, or perhaps sufficient previous experience of having his head nipped, to leave her be.

They pulled into the carpark at Kilmarnock. Ravi turned off the ignition and began checking his messages. Shona shifted, ready to stretch, then the pain reminded her it wasn't a good idea. She got gingerly out of the car and swapped the RNLI fleece she'd worn for the journey for her suit jacket. A stiff breeze was blowing off the Clyde coast, five miles to the west. She looked up at the boxy 1970s, brick-built police station and wrapped a pale blue pashmina around her throat.

'I'll wait for you in reception, shall I, boss?' Ravi twirled the Audi's keys in his long fingers and pushed his fashionably cut dark hair out of his eyes.

Shona nodded. 'If you're not there, I'll bell you.'

'Good luck, boss.'

Deciding she'd had enough of stairs for the day, she took the lift to the top floor. Its doors opened to reveal the deeply carpeted corridor, lined by glass-fronted rooms, most with their vertical blinds closed. Detective Superintendent Clive Davies stood uncertainly on the threshold of his office. He was in his fifties, fit, neat and precise in a mid-range dark suit with close-cropped sandy hair above a high forehead, and he had the habit of pressing his tie against his chest as if the unanchored strip of material might fly off at any minute.

There was a brief handshake, and he ushered her inside.

Coffee was offered and declined.

They faced each other across the barren landscape of Davies's desk. No photographs of family. No personalised mug from the grandkids to keep the darkness at bay and remind him why he still did the job. Her boss looked at her with practised calm, but Shona saw a flicker of unease in the way he straightened his pen and checked his notes, a few short lines that didn't merit his level of scrutiny.

'Something's come in,' he said. 'I'd like you to take it on.'

He slid an A4 sheet across the desk. The letterhead showed the ark-like logo of a British-registered independent film company, Boat Hoose Productions. The name referenced a Glaswegian joke that those who did well in life could move from council accommodation into a 'bought house', rendered by the local accent into *boat hoose*. Shona scanned the document and saw that Lilly

Chase, an American superstar singer and fledgeling actress, was slated to play Robert Burns's wife, Jean Armour. So, Hollywood was coming to town.

Heart of Fire *is a historical drama featuring poet and exciseman Robert Burns, who must take on the most powerful smuggling gang on the Solway coast to rescue his best friend and save himself from the gallows. Faced with the deepest betrayals, both at home and abroad, he struggles between the official justice of his post in King George's Excise, which he has sworn to uphold, and the natural justice demanded by his conscience.*

Shona looked up at her Super. A hand-patting request that she take extended leave, sign off with stress, or otherwise disappear into the woodwork, was what she'd been expecting. However, they couldn't fault her solve rate and her performance reports were up to date, so opportunities to force her out were limited.

'They're shooting in Dumfries and Galloway,' Davies said. 'You're to act as liaison for the production. Smooth out any issues. There's been some stalking threats to one of the actors. A fan was detained at their Hollywood home. Turned out to be armed.'

Shona realised this must be the same production that had hired Tommy McCall's boat.

Shona swallowed and, with effort, parked her expression in neutral. Surely, he wasn't serious. This was a job for the actor's personal protection, or the production's security, and the local police community support team. Closing a few roads, handling residents' gripes about noise and disruption was the long and short of it.

'Sir, I'm not sure why you need a Scottish detective inspector if there's no crime to investigate *here*.' Except one of historical accuracy, Shona thought. Her sergeant, Murdo, was an ardent Robert Burns fan, quick to quote the author of 'Auld Lang Syne' and 'Tam o' Shanter' at length when he'd had a dram or two. She was sure he'd never mentioned anything like this *Poldark*-style romp.

'That's rather the point,' he said, calmly. 'We don't want any incidents.'

'I'm sure Lilly Chase can afford her own private security.'

'The film will be a big boost for local tourism and businesses. And running a CID operation is a high-pressure job. It'll be a break for you. I hear they're planning to film on one of the islands in the Solway. Your boating experience will come in handy.'

Boating experience. He made it sound like she'd taken a yacht for a Sunday sail. The face of the Manxman came back to her: in fear for his life but unable to take the helping hand offered. Is that what she was doing? If the last few months had taught her anything it was that she couldn't do this – job, B&B, Becca's schooling – alone. But if she didn't stick to her course, face down the storm, where would she wash up?

'What about my caseload?' The big-ticket items were an arson attack on a warehouse, probably an insurance job, and a serious assault. The rest were bread and butter – theft, shoplifting, housebreaking and small-scale fraud.

'Sergeant O'Halloran can keep things moving. DI Dalrymple over in Galloway can handle anything big that comes up.'

Shona swallowed again. Behind her eyes was a hard, brittle pressure. If she wasn't careful, she might explode and start screaming at her boss that none of this was her fault, so why was he taking away the one thing she was any good at? She'd done nothing wrong, so why was she the one being punished?

She pushed down the rage. 'This isn't an appropriate use of my time, or the divisional budget, sir.'

Davies straightened his pen and leaned forward with his hands clasped in front of him.

'You need to be realistic, DI Oliver,' he said, his tone hardening. 'You can't just carry on as if nothing has happened. For your own good, take what I'm offering because the alternative is suspension. I don't think you're fully fit for duty. You'll be hard-pressed to argue otherwise. Think of this as a temporary repositioning on compassionate grounds. You're an experienced officer, a credit to the force. We'd hate to lose you.'

It almost sounded convincing. Davies's gaze strayed to Shona's black eye. She could tell him about yesterday's rescue, big up her volunteering, her additional efforts as a public servant, her community engagement, but it felt like wasted effort. If he cared, he'd have asked.

There was no other way to look at it. She was being sidelined.

For the first time, it occurred to her that she might not have a future career with Police Scotland. But she'd moved once, from the City of London Police, so there was no reason she couldn't do it again. There had been offers, notably a specialist role with the MOD police based in Glasgow – her home city and Becca's first choice for university. But now wasn't the time to be making any more changes. She couldn't afford to lose this job.

'So, you'll do it, Shona.' It was less question than statement.

For the second time that day, she'd been backed into a corner, one she liked a whole lot less than not being allowed to drive. She took as deep a breath as she could and sat a little straighter, ignoring the pang of protest from her ribs. She looked Davies in the eye. She wouldn't give him the satisfaction of suspending her.

'Of course. Sir.'

Chapter 5

Shona got the call early the next morning. A fatal house fire in the Summerhill area of the town. She contacted the fire commander for an update. An eight-year-old girl, Taylor Nicolson, had died, her father sustaining serious injuries while attempting to rescue her. The mother and a baby had escaped but were suffering from smoke inhalation. The cause of the blaze was uncertain. Shona dispatched Murdo, telling him she'd meet him there.

When Shona arrived, she paused on the pavement opposite the scene. The two-storey, 1980s semi was identical to all the others in the street, except it was missing most of its roof. Soot smeared the brickwork in upward arcs that stretched across the neighbouring property. The house's upstairs windows were vacant spaces where fire crews had wrenched out the frames in their search for the victims. The winter sky above reflected the palette of washed-out greys, giving the whole scene the impression of a charcoal drawing.

Her sergeant, Murdo O'Halloran, approached, notebook in hand, his expression grave. The lines etched into his face seemed to have deepened since arriving at the scene and his broad rugby player's shoulders bowed under the weight of what he had to say. His playing days were far behind him. With his sweet tooth and tendency to comfort-eat, his stocky frame was running to seed. Days like this made it run faster. He crossed the lawn of the eviscerated home where the innards lay scattered – scorched plastic toys, singed baby clothes, a melted Christmas tree and the shell of a TV. All charred testaments to small acquisitions of family life.

'What are the fire crew saying?' Shona asked, lifting the inner cordon tape for him to pass under.

'Mother and baby got out the rear bedroom window. Neighbours had a ladder,' Murdo replied, his hand raking through his thinning hair as if to prevent an image of their terror lodging in his head. 'The father, Sean Nicolson, went back for the wee girl. That's her bedroom at the front.' Murdo pointed with his pen at the gaping window above the porch. 'Firefighters found them together. The father was on top, protecting the girl. Looks like he'd been overcome by smoke before he could get the window open.'

Shona let the weight of that information dissipate a little before she continued. 'Any theories on the cause of the fire?'

'Started in the hallway, behind the front door.'

Shona frowned. 'Accelerants?'

'They've swabbed for them.' Murdo nodded. Shona didn't need to elaborate to a detective of Murdo's experience.

If someone had poured petrol through the letterbox and set it alight, this would be a very different investigation. The film crew were due to start shooting tomorrow. Until then she was still the DI in charge of active investigations. It was her responsibility to get sufficient evidence to the Procurator Fiscal's office for them to decide if there was a case to answer.

'The name Sean Nicolson mean anything to you?' she said.

Murdo's encyclopaedic knowledge of the criminal population of her patch, gained on his way up from beat cop, was often more accurate than the official records.

He bit his bottom lip, then shook his head. 'The mum's still at the Royal. I've sent Ravi up to talk to her, see if there's been any threats. You heading there next?'

Shona nodded. Ravi would get everything they needed, but as the senior officer, she owed it to the dead girl's family to pay her respects, answer any questions and assure them the matter would be fully investigated.

'Get any background you can on the family,' Shona said quietly. 'Caw canny with the neighbours.' She glanced up at the bystanders, some clutching flowers, most tearful. Murdo would tread carefully, she knew, but it served to underline how important the early stage of an investigation was in keeping the community onside, a reminder that should be emphasised to the uniform constables and volunteer Specials who'd shoulder most of the door-to-door.

'When will we get the report from the SFRS investigation team?' Shona asked. The Scottish Fire and Rescue Service had their own forensic specialists, some of whom Shona could see suited-up and moving about through the empty frame of the living-room window.

'Interim findings tomorrow,' Murdo replied. 'That's quite a keeker you've got, boss.' He indicated her black eye. 'Hope that's no' from yer meeting at Kilmarnock yesterday. If it is, I'd hate to see the other guy.'

Shona suppressed a smile. 'We need to have a chat later about that.'

She'd left Davies's office yesterday with a face like thunder, and had said little to Ravi on the drive home. The DC had probably given Murdo the heads-up that all was not well.

Shona zipped up her jacket. 'Get Kate down to give you a hand.'

Her other detective constable, Kate Irving, an Edinburgh-born geography graduate, had less of Ravi's easy charm with the public, but she was organised and efficient, and would ensure every base was covered.

'I'll see you back at the office, Murdo.' Shona took a last look at the shell of the once-cosy family home. 'Let me know if you turn up anything from the neighbours.'

–

Cornwall Mount police office sat on the outskirts of Dumfries, between the railway line and a run of out-of-town car dealerships, neither of which did much for the view from the second-floor CID room. This brick-and-glass younger cousin of Kilmarnock HQ wouldn't win any architectural awards, but Shona had to admit that day-to-day operations here were easier than at the Grade II listed Snow Hill station in the City of London where she'd once opened her locker to find a rat, of the four-legged variety, happily chewing her sweater.

When Shona reached the top of the stairs, she paused for a minute, hand on hip, grimacing. Her encounter at the hospital with Taylor Nicolson's mother, Sonya, had been gruelling. The woman was in shock, repeatedly reciting the girl's bedtime routine as if it would reset time and result in a different outcome. Shona recognised that desperate urge. Two years ago, Becca had been badly injured in a hit-and-run, and the idea that she might just cease to exist had been so enormous that it eclipsed anything Shona had ever felt before. She'd never forgotten that feeling and whenever she met a grieving parent, she felt the barb afresh, while simultaneously realising how lucky she was to still have her only child.

Shona took shallow gulps of air and straightened. A searing band of hot metal gripped her chest, adding a spike of pain at the top of each breath. Bruised ribs aside, if this was what forty felt like, they could keep it. She'd been neglecting her usual routine of daily runs and a weekly weights session at the gym across the road and knew her fitness was suffering as a result. She made a mental note to sort that, along with all the other things she'd given up recently. Cinema and shopping trips with friends. A glass of wine at the village pub. Meals out. If Rob had been here—

Stop, she told herself, suddenly exasperated by the way she constantly circled back to his absence. If any day should inspire you to count your blessings and be grateful that you still had a living family, it was today. She used to be good at separating work and home life, a cordon sanitaire necessary for the smooth operation of both. Was this age too? No, it was just this perfect storm of circumstances and she needed to get a grip on it before she crumbled completely.

She pushed through the doors of the CID room with more force than she intended, causing the nearest staff to pop up like meerkats above their computer screens, and then duck back down again at the sight of her black eye and stormy expression.

Murdo's desk was in the far corner, where he could see everyone. Ravi's and Kate's desks were in the centre, butted up against each other, forcing them into a sibling-like co-operation neither was happy with. The rest of the workstations were filled by the civilian staff and, at times, the volunteer Special Officers. In the centre, on the back wall, stood an old document cabinet with a kettle on it. A battered tin tray commemorating the 250th anniversary of Robbie Burns's birth held a selection of mugs, half-empty coffee jars and crumpled tea packets. A neglected box of herbal infusions, which Shona was sure Kate had brought with her on her arrival and since left untouched, was slowly biodegrading. Shona was desperate for a coffee, but not that desperate. She'd have to send one of the Specials out in a minute.

Her own desk was in a glass-partitioned office in one corner. She eased off her coat, booted up her laptop and checked her messages. Reports of people-smuggling activity from the Coastguard and Border Force, and a request for a meeting from a Marine Policy and Engagement Officer to discuss Shona's role in the prevention and detection of wildlife crime. There was a tap on the door and Hannah Crawford – a fifty-something civilian data input operator – came in, brandishing Shona's Charles Rennie Mackintosh mug from which the inviting aroma of real coffee sang like an espresso siren.

'If this was the olden days, your ability to read minds would get you burned as a witch,' Shona said, taking the mug gratefully. 'I won't ask you to reveal your sources.'

'Custody sergeant has a secret cafetière,' Hannah replied. 'But put me on the stand and I'll deny all knowledge.' She pulled the edges of her cardigan together and looked Shona over with a practised, motherly eye. 'If I didn't know what you did in your spare time, I'd be referring you to the domestic violence unit.'

'An encounter with a yacht,' Shona replied, sipping the coffee.

'Cocktails on the poop deck?'

'Something like that.'

'What is a poop deck?'

'Haven't the faintest. But I doubt the clue is in the name.' Shona smiled. 'Everything okay here? Where are we with that serious assault?'

Hannah, who was known to have quite a crush on Murdo, was trusted by him to act as den mother when all the detectives were out, and Shona backed that arrangement.

'Murdo gave me the CCTV to review for Kate. It's quite clear it was the victim's brother who assaulted him. No sign of third-party involvement.'

'Okay. Send me the relevant footage. When Kate gets back, we'll get the guy lifted.'

Shona's phone buzzed.

Hannah backed out of the office with a wave. 'I'll let you get on.'

Thanks, Shona mouthed as she checked the screen. It was Becca.

'Oh my God, Mum, you've got to get me a part in this film,' her daughter said without preamble. 'I've signed up to be an extra, but I might not get picked.'

Shona had barely glanced at the briefing document, only enough to register with a roll of her eyes that it was some experimental Robert Burns biopic starring the American actress and singer Lilly Chase. She'd googled the woman, noted the online abuse she'd received and made it a priority to speak to her about her personal security.

'They're looking for women under thirty with long, undyed hair,' Becca continued. 'Suppose it's because it's set ages ago.'

'Don't suppose they had nose piercings back then either.'

'I could take it out,' Becca said. 'Or they can cover it with a wart – everyone had warts then, didn't they?'

'Well, since you're supposed to be studying a history of medicine module, I'll bow to your greater knowledge on ancient warts.'

Becca ignored the sarcasm and ploughed on. 'And you didn't tell me James McGowan is in it. His big-budget superhero movies and romcoms are okay, but I liked him in *The Last Wolf of Scotland* as an eco-time-traveller who returns to 1745. Redcoats want to shoot him as a Jacobite, but he escapes and smuggles a wee wolf puppy aboard a ship to Canada and sets it free. Quite violent, not really a film for kids. Anyway, Mum, Wiki says he went to your school, so you can definitely get me a part.'

Shona hadn't seen the wolf movie, but the mention of James McGowan had sent her on a time-travelling journey of her own. A tiny burst of queasy excitement flared in her stomach, but she quickly suppressed it.

Jazza Mac G – as she'd known him, then – had been in the year above her at school, and the subject of a brief schoolgirl crush. Over the years, a cinema poster or magazine interview had served as a periodic reminder, but she doubted he'd given her a second thought. He'd left for London straight after finishing his exams, as she'd later done herself. Although not ashamed of her roots in one of Glasgow's worst housing schemes, it was a part of her life she had been glad to escape, and one she still had no desire to revisit.

'He won't remember me,' Shona said. 'And what about your studies?'

'It's perfect. I can ask folk on the movie about the poetry guy. They'll know all sorts of stuff if they're doing a film, right? I can put it all in my essay. It'll be brilliant and so original I'll get an A.'

'By poetry guy I suppose you mean Scotland's national bard, Robert Burns.'

'Yeah, him. Just say yes, Mum. I'll get paid. We could do with the money, couldn't we?'

Ouch.

'I'm not discussing this now,' Shona said.

'I'm doing pasta for dinner,' Becca said. 'Talk then. Bye.'

Shona was left staring at her phone screen. Becca hadn't shown this much enthusiasm for anything in months. She was torn between her desire to see her daughter happy and the sense that it would be a massive distraction from her studies, which would lead to panicky tears and tantrums later.

Nothing could be resolved until she got home so Shona put it from her mind and worked through her actions list until Murdo arrived back, with Ravi and Kate in tow. She called everyone together and Murdo led the update on the fatal house fire. Sean Nicolson's life hung in the balance. His wife could think of no one who would do such a thing to her family, but Kate had found a mixed response from the door-to-door, including arguments over cars blocking access that had resulted in some pushing and shoving.

'Good, Kate. I want you to follow that up.'

It wouldn't be the first time an argy-bargy over parking had resulted in an unbalanced individual deciding to

43

resolve the dispute by visiting violence on their neigh-bours.

'One thing…' Shona began, then outlined that she'd be away for a few weeks on a liaison job, and DI Dalrymple from neighbouring Galloway would be covering. There were frowns and mutterings, but she quelled them by not inviting questions and instructing everyone to get back to their tasks. Kate was already on her phone.

'Ravi, Murdo, a word in my office,' Shona said.

Once there, she expanded on the secondment, but didn't invite speculation on Detective Superintendent Clive Davies's long-term plans for her.

'Aye well, they picked the right time of year to make the film,' Murdo said. 'It'll be Burns Night soon. And just after the mid-winter solstice, when the veil between the worlds grows thin and the devil rides oot with aw his witches and servants.'

Shona and Ravi exchanged a glance. 'You awright there, Murdo?' Ravi said, cocking an eyebrow at his sergeant.

'Oh, aye. Fine,' Murdo replied. 'There's nothing like a good ghost story, at this time of year, eh?' He clapped the palms of his hands together and rubbed them with vigour, beaming at his unsettled audience. 'Had you going there, didn't I?' He grinned. 'Just imagine it, gathered roon the fire with a wee dram. It's a good night oot. Robert Burns was a man who knew about being tormented by devils. Folk had to make their own entertainment before the days of thon Netflix and the like.'

'Aye, I know, but haggis?' Ravi looked doubtful.

'They do a vegetarian one now,' Shona offered.

'Now that is the work of the devil,' Murdo said, shaking his head. 'Don't you mention that in my hearing. Vegetarian haggis,' he muttered, 'nae such thing. What's wrong wi' a sheep's bag stuffed with all the innards and a good bit of seasoning? Nothing wasted.'

'Oh my God!' Ravi made a face. 'Just the thought is enough to make you boak.'

'Well, don't boak in here,' Shona said. 'Your new boss won't want evidence of your lunch on the carpet.'

At the prospect of her absence, both men's faces became sombre, and Shona regretted her comment.

'This isn't going to be a permanent thing, is it?' Ravi said. Now the subject of Shona's secondment was out in the open, Ravi was free to challenge her decision in accepting Davies's order. 'Sure you want to do this?'

Before Shona could answer, Murdo intervened. 'It's not the boss's choice. Best to do what Davies says. No point in getting his goat, just at the minute.' He turned to Shona. 'We'll keep everything running here till you get back, boss. And you know we're only on the end of a phone, both of us.' He looked pointedly at Ravi, who gave an obedient nod. 'All of us. That goes for Kate too.'

'Thanks, Murdo,' Shona said quietly.

'Fresh faces might do you the world of good,' Murdo added. 'Even if they are actors.'

'Well, Kate's a drama queen, so you've had plenty of practice.' Ravi grinned.

Shona glanced through the glass partition, out into the main office where DC Kate Irving sat at her desk. As if summoned by some supernatural sense that she was once more the subject of Ravi's sharp wit, she looked at him with narrowed eyes. Ravi grinned at her.

'Just you two behave yourselves while I'm not here,' Shona said.

'Don't worry, boss. It'll be fine,' said Murdo, and Shona almost believed him.

Tomorrow she'd be on the film set and they'd all have to make the best of it.

Chapter 6

The Dumfries house that was once Robert Burns's family home stood in the last fragment of a street whose ends had long since frayed away. The two-storey weathered red sandstone building, now a museum, retained an apron of cobbles which quickly met tarmac outside an adjacent nursery school. At the other side of the building were council flats and a carpark packed tight with panel vans and the film crew's Winnebagos. A sharp rain shower had passed, leaving the cobbles slick and shining in the low winter light. Becca was supposedly studying and hadn't raised the subject of an extra's role again, but Shona had seen the movie extras agency's app open on her phone.

At least the whole site would be easy to lock down, thought Shona, as she made her way towards two security staff in black cargo pants and bomber jackets, monitoring a small group of female fans pressed up against the temporary Heras fencing. The young women seemed to move as one, like the leaves of a single tree. They swayed on tiptoe and displayed a collective flutter in response to any breeze of set activity that indicated their idol, American singer Lilly Chase, might appear.

Shona had vacillated between a formal business suit that might emphasise her position and authority, and something more casual. In the end, she'd opted for jeans, a fleece and waterproof jacket. A few years back, in London, she'd completed a close protection course and knew the value of blending in while she scoped out any potential threats. Perhaps Superintendent Davies had spotted this in her file. But if he thought dangling celebrities before her was all it would take to shift her from the frontline job she loved, he was mistaken.

Shona showed her warrant card to a man whose heavily muscled shoulders formed a distinct triangle with his waist. He let her through and pointed out the director, who stood in front of the museum, like a stepping-stone in the middle of a burn, as activity flowed around him. He was scrolling through a tablet balanced on top of an armful of paperwork, a mobile phone tucked between ear and shoulder. Further on, lights and equipment were being guided past a group of extras in period costume gathered around a wagon.

The director, Simon Jones, wore jeans and a dark hoodie under a battered, brown leather jacket. An unbranded baseball cap covered his shaven head. Shona waited until he'd ended his call and returned to his paper-work, then introduced herself. He frowned, the lines around his eyes giving him a look of irritation, as if she'd interrupted him in some deep intellectual questioning of the meaning of life. Then he seemed to realise who she was and why she was there, and the clouds lifted.

'DI Oliver, yes? It's fantastic to meet you,' he said, juggling his papers then pumping her hand, a broad smile wiping a decade off his face. 'Can't tell you how grateful we are that someone of your seniority and experience has agreed to take us under their wing.'

'Not how I'd have described it,' Shona replied.

'Absolutely no slight intended, DI Oliver,' he said, anxiously, in a soft Edinburgh accent.

Shona smiled. 'None taken.' She immediately liked this earnest and empathetic young man: his job probably included a similar level of cat herding to her own.

'How are things going? Any trouble?' Shona said, as she stepped aside to let a man dressed as an eighteenth-century carter walk past.

Simon shrugged. 'A few fans got into the hotel rooms. There was no damage. Our security and your uniform colleagues gave them a warning,' he said with a nod towards the knot of young women at the fence. 'It's fine. We don't want any negative publicity with arrests. The weather's putting off all but the die-hards.' He shivered and pulled the zip of his hoodie up under his chin. 'We'll be out of here tomorrow. The other locations are less accessible. Of course, the Chasers are all over this on social media.'

Lilly Chase's army of fans had quickly become embroiled in a spat with a critic who'd questioned their idol's fitness as an actor, mobbing the magazine he worked for. Social media gave an illusion of access and intimacy. Fans' online behaviour could quickly escalate because they thought they were defending a friend. Soon it was death threats to anyone who threw shade on their beloved.

'I'd like to talk to Ms Chase,' Shona said. 'But first, can you give me more details on your shooting plans?'

The briefing document had lived up to its name – brief. The blurb about the film's content was followed by two sparse pages. Three weeks' shooting, four principal locations. Permits for road closures and on-set firearms were in place. Public liability insurance documents attached.

'Ah, yes.' Simon rifled among his bundle and handed her a slim document stapled in one corner. 'Apologies.

Here's the shooting script. It's like a blueprint for the production. Quite a bit thinner than we'd normally use, but James wants to improvise his scenes. He's read everything there is to read and even bought some of Burns's possessions at auction for huge sums. The other actors have their own scripts with their lines, of course, but he'll be responding as he believes Burns would have done, in order to give a more spontaneous atmosphere to the film.'

Shona had no idea if this was common practice but in her experience a lack of planning led to a lack of progress. That was their lookout. The sheets listed scenes, times, locations and actors present. What, when, where and who. She didn't need to know the why. A few spots of rain fell on the paper. Two women hurried past, putting up umbrellas which were held above the extras, while a couple had the added protection of shower caps pulled over their wigs.

'Lilly is in the bedroom,' Simon said, indicating the upstairs window. He was jostled by two men, wheeling a barrel on a bogey, who called out an apology. 'Come up,' he said to Shona. 'We're just resetting the deathbed scene for a final take.'

'Don't the museum mind you traipsing all over the house?' Shona said as they threaded their way to the front door where the original stone steps had been overlaid with a temporary ramp to facilitate the heavy camera equipment.

'Our fee will cover their running costs for the next three years.' Simon grinned. 'James felt it was important to use authentic locations and they don't get more authentic than this. The Burns family lived here from 1793 until he died.' He lowered his voice. 'As exec producer, James is bankrolling the project. It's his baby. A move away from big-budget roles and back to his acting roots. He's even had a falling-out with his agent over it. And we're getting Lilly for a song, no pun intended. They're friends, and she's keen to broaden her range.' He put out a hand, indicating Shona should precede him up the narrow stair. 'And the museum will get a flood of visitors when the film comes out.'

Shona squeezed into a sparse room which already contained about a dozen people, including two young children. The illumination from the single sash window had been supplemented by a bank of LEDs, which reflected softly off the limewashed walls and bare floorboards. Lilly Chase sat on the edge of a wooden box-bed that filled one corner of the room and seemed to emit a light all her own. She wore a simple linen nightdress, which might have looked like a dishrag on anyone else, and a blue woollen shawl that caught the intense colour of her eyes. Her customary blonde hair had been dyed a fiery red, although Shona seemed to recall Jean Armour's portrait showed her with mousey brown hair. There was a final touch-up of Lilly's make-up and Simon pronounced they were ready for a take.

As the camera rolled, Lilly leaned onto the bed, her face suddenly a mask of grief as the two children ran forward and clutched at her. Outside, a cacophony of street noises, with clatters and bangs from the kitchen downstairs, contributed to a chaotic home atmosphere. When the male voice came, Shona felt a jolt. From her position by the door, she hadn't realised James McGowan, or rather Robert Burns, was in the box-bed. Perhaps with a worldwide audience in mind, authenticity didn't stretch to dialogue in the historical Scots tongue and Ayrshire accent of Burns. Instead, the harsher tones of their shared Glaswegian past were blunted just enough so that the film wouldn't need the additional expense of subtitles.

Shona found her disinclination to engage with the film-making process quickly ebbed as the scene unfolded. The bustle of the crew settled to a kind of hushed watchfulness as if, at the magic word *action*, the spark of life had flowed out of them and become concentrated in the actors. McGowan was an ethereal voice reaching out to her from the past, and Lilly's luminous presence turned the room from monochrome to colour. Shona stood transfixed, breath held. When a heart-rending cry of anguish from Lilly filled the room and brought the deathbed scene to a close, Shona felt a welling of sympathy for the widowed Jean, and quickly blinked away if not a tear, then certainly an embarrassed moistening of her eye.

'Cut,' Simon called. 'Lilly, that was beautiful. James, perfection as always. Guys, you were great.' He gave the children a thumbs up and they smiled shyly. 'We're moving on to the tavern scene. Thank you, everyone.'

As the make-up woman crossed to Lilly and helped her to her feet, the bed curtain was thrown back and James McGowan, in breeches and a stained shirt, appeared, his face pale and lined. He staggered towards the door and Shona instinctively put out a hand to steady him, but he brushed past without acknowledging her. She drew back her hand quickly, as if he'd slapped her, feeling unaccountably hurt and angered by his rejection.

'Don't worry.' Simon was at her shoulder, as the actor vanished down the stairs. 'It's not intentional rudeness. He likes to remain in character while on set. It helps with the flow of improvisation. Come on, I'll introduce you to Lilly. She's less… method.' He grinned.

At five feet four inches, Shona knew she was dubbed 'Wee Shona' by her CID team, although no one would dare say it within earshot of her. So it was a surprise to realise that, in contrast to her larger-than-life stage persona, Lilly Chase was tiny: a good three inches shorter than Shona. But the bird-like frailty of her bones was tempered by the toned, iron-hard sculpting of the muscles that overlaid them. Shona could see how this woman, for all her big voice and even bigger personality, might become the target of misguided individuals driven by a warped desire to 'protect', and thereby take ownership of, their doll-like idol.

After the introductions, Simon and the rest of the crew left, keen to get on. Lilly was not needed. It was a tavern scene next. The house opposite the museum had been repurposed as a howff.

'So, you're the DI?' Lilly said, taking Shona's hand in her firm grip. *Dee-eye*. The drawn-out syllables made Shona wonder if she was being mocked. 'This gig's way below your pay grade,' Lilly continued. 'Babysitting actors.' *Act-tors*. There it was again, perhaps just the consequence of her New York accent. 'Why ya doin' it?'

Shona was surprised that an American understood ranks within British policing. She could have given her the spiel – facilitating closer ties with the cultural community and ensuring the smooth operation of an important tourist boost. But she sensed Lilly was too sharp for that.

'My boss didn't give me a choice.'

'Well, he sounds like a jerk. Lord knows we've met plenty of them.' She gave Shona a complicit smile. 'I had my people check you out. I'm sorry your husband is in jail, babe. Did he do it?'

Shona stared, momentarily wrong-footed by this woman's directness and unhappy at being called 'babe' by someone ten years her junior.

'No, he didn't do it,' Shona said stiffly. 'He placed his trust in the wrong individuals. We're preparing an appeal.'

'Hey, no judgement. Guys put you through it, don't they, sister? Shit, my last boyfriend tried to post a sex tape. What a bastard. Can you believe it?'

Shona stopped breathing. How could Lilly possibly know about what Delfont had done to her and about the threat of the recording of the assault ending up in the public domain that had hung over her for more than two years.

'Babe? You okay?' Lilly took hold of Shona's arm.

'Yes, yes. I'm fine.' Shona forced herself to smile. It was clear from the singer's expression that she didn't know. It seemed they had more in common than Lilly realised. 'I need to go over your personal security,' Shona said.

'Oh, don't worry about that. My team are the best, been with me years. They'd eat anyone who came within ten feet of me. I'm dead-ass serious here. It's why they checked you out.'

'What about the break-in at your house?' Shona said.

'There's been a break-in? What the fuck! No one told me.'

'I thought you were there. Last month? A fan pulled a gun on you.'

A look of relief washed over Lilly as she shook her head. 'No, sis. That wasn't me. That was James. He's the one you need to talk to.'

'Oh,' Shona said, momentarily embarrassed her preparation had lacked its customary rigour. If Lilly noticed, she didn't comment on it.

Instead, she said, 'Say, can I call you if I need character background? I'm up for a role in some British cop show. An NYPD cop relocates to Yorkshire.'

'Yes. Sure,' Shona replied, not at all sure why she was agreeing, but Lilly was already breezing out.

'Thanks, sis.'

Moments later, Shona heard the squeals from the fans by the gate that heralded Lilly's return to her Winnebago.

—

Shona left the museum and went through the open front door of the house opposite. At some point the room's plaster had been removed, revealing the original stone-work. With the barrels, oil lamps and wooden bar top, it made a convincing drinking den. Shona watched as a drunken Robert Burns caroused with his friends, sang a song he'd composed and groped the barmaid. How many children had he fathered in and out of wedlock? Twelve by four different women, and that's just the ones history knew about. She checked the shooting script. The scene was titled, *Burning the candle at both ends.* That about summed things up. Despite Becca's enthusiasm, Shona didn't want her anywhere near this caper.

The improvised scene continued until James climbed upon a barrel and began swinging from the roof beam. The other actors and extras seemed bemused by this turn of events and the action ground to a halt, leaving McGowan suspended awkwardly in mid-air.

'Cut there,' Simon called. 'James, I'm not sure this is going anywhere.'

McGowan dropped to the ground.

If Shona had been in a better mood, it would almost have been funny. But the magic she'd felt watching the deathbed scene had evaporated, and she felt foolish that she'd been so taken in by the novelty and superficial glamour of the film set. Her ribs were throbbing, and she was no closer to her objectives in establishing security protocols.

Finally, after several takes, Simon announced a short break to adjust the lighting. Shona took a deep breath and approached McGowan, who had his arm around the shoulder of an actor in uniform, whose face was vaguely familiar. She held out her hand.

'Hello, I'm DI Shona Oliver.'

McGowan looked at her blearily. 'Ah, the law! Conjured to oppress all honest folk.'

Shona glared at him. He obviously didn't recognise her, and she wasn't going to suck up to him by alluding to their shared schooldays. 'I need to talk to you about your security.'

Shona felt a hand under her elbow and turned to see Simon's anxious face. He drew her aside as McGowan launched into another song.

'*Is there, for honest poverty, that hings his head, an' a' that,*' McGowan sang and was immediately joined by a raucous cheer from the crowd. Shona knew the song too, one of Burns's most famous. 'A Man's a Man, for A' That'. A poor honest man was worth more than any lord. Becca sometimes played a version by Paolo Nutini, which at this moment Shona found she definitely preferred.

'I'm so sorry,' Simon said, raising his voice to be heard. 'Literally no point in trying to talk to him now, while he's concentrating on his character. I'll get his assistant to schedule a chat later. Will that be okay?' He gave her a pleading look. 'We'll be here until we lose the light. I'm sorry it's such a waste of your time. Why don't you get some coffee?'

Shona stomped back down to the Winnebago village, stopping only to ask the site security if mobile CCTV was in operation, but Lilly Chase's own team were already on it. She'd expected Boat Hoose to pay attention to what she had to say, to take her advice regarding security seriously, but it felt more like her presence was a box-ticking exercise. The director was right. What a waste of time.

Chapter 7

Shona took the mug of coffee from the lunch truck and washed down a couple of painkillers. She stood near the gathered fans, committing their faces to memory. While a couple of them were Chasers – they were clearly fans of Lilly, as evidenced by their outlandish dress: a hat made of metal spoons, pink PVC dungarees – most, she now realised, were probably in McGowan's camp.

One, who'd obviously clocked Shona's access to the set, sidled up to her.

'Have you seen James this morning? How is he?' It was hard to guess the woman's age. She could have been anywhere from twenty to forty, slightly built, with dyed blonde hair and a crop top under clothing too thin for January. Her accent wasn't local.

'Where are you from?' Shona asked, ignoring the woman's question. The other fans, scenting opportunity, had gathered round. *London*, *Luton*, *Hemel Hempstead*, came the replies.

'James likes us to be here when he's working,' a young, round-faced woman in jeans and a fitted jacket said. 'Says we're good for his spiritual energy. He always thanks me on Instagram when I post stuff.'

'He always likes my tweets,' a blonde woman cut in, a competitive edge evident in her tone.

Probably one of his assistants, Shona thought, but didn't say.

'Do you know where he's going for dinner tonight?' Crop-Top said. 'Or will he be at the hotel? Will he order room service, do you think?'

Shona produced her warrant card. 'I don't know if any of you ladies were involved in last night's fun and games, but just so we understand each other, I take a dim view of any lawbreaking. Next time, it won't be a warning. While trespass under Scots law is often a civil matter, I will arrest anyone attempting to access Ms Chase's or Mr McGowan's hotel room, or otherwise making a nuisance of themselves, as a breach of the peace. That's up to twelve months in prison or a £5000 fine, or both. Am I making myself clear?'

The women looked suddenly taken aback, as if they'd never consider such behaviour unreasonable; however, most nodded. Perhaps if they knew what he was really like, Shona thought, their enthusiasm would wane. But, given the level of obsession that caused you to travel hundreds of miles at your own expense, only to freeze your tits off for the briefest glimpse of a self-obsessed arsehole like James McGowan, she doubted it.

'And,' she continued, 'there will also be an interdict banning you from coming within one hundred metres of James McGowan or contacting him in any way, including social media.'

That seemed to have a more sobering effect.

Shona returned her cup to the catering wagon where crew members were beginning to queue up. She checked her watch. It would soon be lunchtime. The light was already on its steady decline towards four p.m., when it would be snuffed out completely. Her phone, turned to silent on the set, showed a stack of missed calls. A few were from Rob's barrister, Anoushka, another from a member of the B&B owners' group, and the others she didn't recognise. Her finger hovered over Anoushka's call, then she pulled up Murdo's number and hit that instead.

'Boss.' Murdo answered on the first ring. 'How's it going?'

'Don't ask,' Shona replied. She thought of reeling off the morning's debacle, the lack of original Scots dialogue, but Murdo would take to heart the liberties visited upon Scotland's national bard, so why ruin his day? It would be months, if not years, before the film came out. She could give him her review later and save him the price of a cinema ticket. 'Has the new DI settled in okay?'

Murdo hesitated. 'Aye, all fine here. Dalrymple is happy to stay in Galloway. I've just to update him, as and when. Sure he'll be over in person at some point.'

She wasn't going to openly criticise another inspector to Murdo but they both knew it was shoddy. The family of the girl killed in yesterday's house fire deserved a senior officer on the ground. The investigation was still at a crucial early stage and, capable as Murdo was, as a detective sergeant he shouldn't have been shouldering this amount of responsibility.

'Any update on the fire?' Shona said.

'Father is still critical. The initial report's just in. No accelerant found. No cause identified yet. Mum and baby are being discharged to temp accommodation later today. I'm putting together an interim file for the fiscal. Ravi's just on his way back from updating the mum.'

Shona pressed her lips together, thinking. She checked the time again. 'I've done all I need to here. Why don't we grab a sandwich? My treat. Then we can pop up to the hospital and have a chat with the mother. See how she's coping.'

'Aye,' replied Murdo. 'That's no' a bad idea.'

If it turned out later that the family were unhappy with the police investigation, it wouldn't be the Galloway DI that came in for flak, it would be Dumfries CID. For that reason, as much as common humanity, the mother deserved an hour of Shona's time, and any assistance she and Murdo were able to give that would smooth her and her family's path to recovery.

–

Shona met Murdo in the carpark of Dumfries and Galloway Royal Infirmary. She slotted her Audi into a space, then got in the passenger side of Murdo's Astra and handed him a coronation chicken sandwich, an iced bun and a large tea, while she tucked into a ham and mustard on wholemeal. They chatted between bites and Shona fielded Murdo's questions about the filming with bland answers, tamping down the anger and humiliation she felt at her encounter with that total eejit McGowan and her posting to the job in the first place. God, how embarrassing was it to think she'd actually fancied him at school.

When she and Murdo had finished the sandwiches, they walked together to the hospital's front entrance. Needle points of rain hit their faces, while the buffeting wind made further conversation impossible.

Sonya Nicolson sat on a plastic chair in the hospital corridor, ten-month-old Noah on her knee. Shona thought the woman looked hollowed out, and her tired smile at the police officers' arrival was clearly a knee-jerk reaction that didn't extend to her red-rimmed eyes.

Beyond was the room where her husband, Sean, lay, the severity of his injuries requiring an induced coma.

'I know I can't see him,' Sonya said as Shona took the seat next to her. 'But where else would I be?' She'd retained the look of bewilderment that Shona had seen the day before. She was wearing her hospital dressing gown, but over joggers and a pink T-shirt, a sidestep towards her discharge later that afternoon.

'Sonya, shall we go and get some coffee?' Shona said. She smiled and put out her hands to baby Noah, who automatically lifted his own in response, happy to be held by this stranger. Shona scooped him up as Murdo helped the mother to her feet.

They found a quiet space in the family room and Shona settled the baby back into his mother's lap. Murdo returned with coffee.

'How's Sean?' Shona said.

'Still alive,' Sonya responded. 'They say it's good he's made it this far, but he's no' gonnae be oot soon. I dinnae know what to do about Taylor's funeral.'

Sonya kept glancing at the space on each side of her chair, the automatic behaviour of a parent checking on the whereabouts of their child. Shona felt a pang each time Sonya was hit by the renewed grief that her daughter would never need checking on again.

'You don't need to decide anything now,' Shona said gently. 'There'll be a wee bit of a delay, 'cos of the investigation anyway. Have you any family that can help?'

'Aye, ma sister and her husband are on their way fae Aberdeen. They'll be here tonight.'

Noah, who'd been happily smiling at Murdo, began to cough and grizzle. To Shona's surprise, Murdo, who had no children of his own, took the child from his mother's knee and placed him over his shoulder, patting his back while distracting him with the colours in the vending machine.

'Ravi will have told you we're still looking into the cause of the fire,' Shona said, 'and that there was no accelerant, like petrol, found. Can you remember what was in the hall, near the front door?' Shona leaned forward and covered Sonya's hand with her own. Ravi would also have posed that question, but often people recalled details later, when the shock had worn off a little. 'You're not in any trouble. No one is saying the fire is your, or your family's, fault.'

'The fire people wanted tae know that, too. There wis nothing in the hall 'cept bags and coats. We dinnae smoke.' An edge of defiance had crept into Sonya's voice. 'Nae candles 'cos of the bairns, like.'

'And there's no one you can think of that might have done this deliberately?' It would still have been possible, though less likely, to set the fire without accelerant, using matches and paper.

Sonya looked up at Noah as if checking the baby wasn't listening in. 'It's just...' she began. 'Taylor's dad. He doesnae have any contact wi' her. Didnae,' she corrected herself. 'But I know he's back.'

It was evident to Shona, from the way Sonya shifted awkwardly in her seat, that the mere mention of Taylor's father stirred up a deep visceral fear in her.

'Sean isn't Taylor's birth father?' Shona said, aware that Murdo was listening in and making a mental note of this detail.

'No. His name's Joe Dylan.' Sonya was knotting a tissue to shreds in her hand. 'I'm no' saying it wis him.'

'Where's Joe been?' Shona asked, feeling that she wasn't going to like the reply.

'Inside. Five year.'

'What for?'

'Arson.'

'Okay, thank you.' Shona took a card from her wallet and handed it to Sonya, trying hard to ignore the clamour of self-reproach sounding in her head. Joe Dylan was a day-one detail they should have picked up straight away. 'Call me, anytime, if you think of something, or if I can help in any way.'

When they'd said their goodbyes, Shona and Murdo headed back to the carpark.

'How did we miss that?' Murdo muttered, his phone already clamped to his ear.

Shona shook her head. 'I know. I suppose there was no reason we'd connect them.'

'Aye, well, we've connected them now, and Joe Dylan will be getting his door chapped.'

Shona nodded. Despite the emotional pain she'd just encountered, Shona knew this was where she belonged, where she could do some good. This was real life, not the fake one she'd witnessed on the film set. You want authentic, she thought, conjuring up James McGowan in her mind's eye. Well, this is about as authentic as it gets.

–

Shona and Murdo got back to their cars just as the heavens opened. He waved to her as he drove off back to the office. The traffic was at a standstill at the carpark exit and, through the driving rain, she saw Murdo's brake lights come on. She started her engine but didn't pull out, waiting for the misted windscreen, and the exit queue, to clear a little. As she glanced at her phone, she remembered the missed calls and hit the reply button for Rob's barrister. She'd sorted most of Rob's papers from the boxes in the garage, entering them into a timeline and spreadsheet, but was making frustratingly slow progress uncovering anything useful. She felt a stab of guilt that the task had been placed somewhat on the back burner over the last few days, due to police work, and vowed to devote a few hours to completing her preliminary enquiries when she got back to High Pines.

'Hi, Anoushka, how are you? Sorry, I meant to ring you back earlier, but I got caught up.'

'Are you at home, Shona?'

'Heading that way. I'm just in the car.' She had twice-weekly phone calls with Rob, who had recently discouraged her from taking two days out of her schedule to make the gruelling monthly visit to Wandsworth in south-west London, saying she'd wear herself out. If Anoushka had news about an appeal, he hadn't mentioned it.

'Listen, I don't want you to worry. Rob's fine, but you should know, he's in the prison hospital wing. He's been attacked.'

An iron fist, cold and unyielding, gripped Shona's heart. 'What! What happened? Is he badly hurt?'

'Bruising, mostly, but he has fractures to the metacarpal bones of his right hand. Someone stamped on it. He says he doesn't know who.'

'Was it a fight?' She couldn't imagine Rob picking a fight, but he might stand up for someone else who was being bullied. At school he'd played rugby, but at university he'd rowed, joking he'd had enough of contact sports by then.

'I don't think so. He's playing it down, but he's shaken,' Anoushka said. 'Shona, I'm sorry to have to say this, but it may just be because his wife is a police officer.'

She'd been a fool to think they could keep that quiet. She'd hoped her being in Dumfries would give him some protection. But she'd been a cop in London – not the Met, but close enough for anyone who thought they had an old score to settle.

'We have to get him out,' Shona said.

'We will. I'm looking at some potential new evidence, but I want to confirm before we discuss it,' Anoushka said. 'Shona. There's something else. A friend from the chambers preparing to prosecute DCI Harry Delfont has just been told by the CPS that they're dropping the case.'

Shona stared at the windscreen of her car as the heavy raindrops detonated on the glass. She scrambled to recalibrate in her head what this meant for Rob's future appeal, for Becca, for the other women Delfont had attacked, for her job, for the B&B and, lastly, for herself, until it all tumbled into a great broiling pot of rage.

'I'm sorry, Shona. I'd like to say I can't believe it, but unfortunately, I can. Look, Rob's got an extra phone card. He's due to call you tonight, around seven p.m.'

Shona would be home by then, plenty of time to figure out her next move. She'd get a visiting order, be there by the end of the week. The staff would already be assessing him as a vulnerable prisoner, maybe getting him moved out of London, closer to Scotland. Wandsworth housed Category B prisoners and was one of the most overcrowded prisons in Britain. The high value of Rob's money-laundering offence had placed him with those convicted of threat-to-life crimes, drugs, sexual and firearms offences: prisoners with potential access to millions had a higher risk of escape and needed more security.

'We'll talk more tomorrow,' the barrister said.

'Thanks, Anoushka,' was all Shona could manage.

She hurried back to High Pines from the hospital, not wanting to risk Rob ringing their home phone early and catching Becca before she had time to prepare her for the news. In the end, she needn't have worried. Becca's text arrived as Shona turned off the main road toward Kirkness village. She was over at Ravi and Martin's, seeing about some homework, and would be back after tea. Shona paced the room, unable to eat the pasta bake Becca had left, until finally, Rob called.

He downplayed the incident, just as Anoushka had said, but Shona wasn't fooled.

'Rob, your injuries were bad enough to put you in the hospital wing. I'm coming to see for myself.'

'No, don't. It's nothing. You've had worse on the life-boat.'

Shona touched her black eye. If this was a FaceTime call, he'd have plenty to back up his argument. What were they like, the pair of them? Battered and bruised, but for different reasons. For Shona, it was a reminder of a life saved. For Rob, a reminder of a life in danger.

Now didn't seem the right time to tell him that the charges against Delfont had been dropped. No one from the police investigation, Operation Vita, or the Crown Prosecution Service had been in touch, and part of her clung to the idea that Anoushka's friend had got it wrong. Hope was what they both needed now.

'I'm going through the evidence. I'm sure I'll find something on Delfont we can use for an appeal, but until then, you need to go into segregation.'

'Not a chance. I'm not being banged up with all the paedophiles and rapists. I'm not having people think I'm one of them. And I'd be no safer in there.'

'What d'you mean?' Shona said, puzzled. 'You may not have a choice. The governor must already consider you a vulnerable prisoner. You're the husband of a serving police officer.'

'Nobody knows that.'

'You're kidding me. They know. If it wasn't all around the prison beforehand, it will be now.'

'Look, we need to shelve the idea of an appeal for a bit,' Rob said. 'Let things settle down.' He was pleading now.

'Who did this, Rob? And don't tell me you don't know.' She could hear her own voice rising, frustration edged with fear.

'Just let it go, Shona.'

'Tell me, because you know I'm not going to let *anything* go unless you give me a very good reason.'

'Becca,' said Rob quietly. 'Becca is the reason you need to drop this, darlin'. If I appeal, they'll come after you both. It's not just Delfont. It's whatever gang he was working with. If I stay quiet, we'll be fine, and that's all that matters now. If you stir things up again, they'll come for us all, but Becca will be first. That's what they said.'

She was numb with shock. Not just at the attack on Rob, but what it might mean for her precious daughter.

'You need to do something for me, Shona.'

'What?'

'You need to look after our girl.'

Chapter 8

When Becca came home, Shona told her the bare details of what had happened to her father and reassured her that Rob was fine. A scuffle, damage to his hand. He'd live to cook another day. A feeble joke. Becca was tearful and wanted to see Rob immediately. A visit was tricky, Shona said, but she could talk to him on the phone tomorrow night.

Rob had been sentenced to ten years. With parole, he'd serve five inside, and the rest on licence. The warning not to pursue an appeal meant he was a threat to someone. Even five years was too long to be looking over your shoulder. The criminal gang behind the fraud had never been identified, but it was evident their web extended inside the prison walls, and the threat wasn't just confined to Rob. If Becca was a target too, Shona had to act. But how?

She could confide in Murdo or Ravi, or even Dan Ridley – a Cumbrian detective constable who'd been a rock for her in previous cases – but she'd only be laying her burden on them. And there were other issues to consider, too. She knew that, to protect her, Murdo would surely flag it to Superintendent Davies, handing her boss the perfect excuse to pull her from active service on the grounds of her own safety. And with the case against Delfont dropped, he was once more a credible threat to her professional reputation. Rob was tucked up in jail, so her former boss would come after her now. She was still a serving officer, and he knew that she knew he was corrupt. The longer he left her in post, the greater the threat that she'd uncover something to bring him down. If he leaked the film of her assault – Shona gave an involuntary shudder – the trail would lead right back to him. So what else was he prepared to do to finish her? Kill Rob? She had no faith the prison authorities could protect him. They hadn't so far. The only way to protect him would be to get him out of jail. And the only person who could do that was her.

Shona had wrestled with this for most of a sleepless night, and at one point she left her bed to review Rob's financial records. But the numbers jumped about the page, until she gave up. Eventually, she dropped off after four a.m., only to be woken less than two hours later by her regular alarm. She needed to be up anyway. The film crew were due to begin shooting at Hildan Island that morning. The place was privately owned, with an old manor house built for a fourteenth-century Scottish noble, but no year-round human inhabitants. It was no surprise to her that the promised meeting with McGowan to discuss personal security hadn't materialised. In some ways, that was a relief. She wasn't sure she'd get through it without giving him a free character reading. *Were you really such an arsehole at school, or is it something you've been working on?*

At least the island location was naturally more secure. Tommy McCall had taken some of the camera and lighting team across the night before and she was hitching a lift on the *Silver Crest* that morning, along with the remaining equipment. It had stopped raining, but the wind was still up. The main actors were arriving by launch. She hoped they had their sea legs.

She'd just eased on a layer of thermals, before pulling a sweater over her bruised ribs, when she heard the gate buzzer sound in the kitchen. Who on earth would be calling at this time in the morning? She padded downstairs. The security camera screen showed a dark panel van. A man stood, hood up, with his back to the camera. Shona felt unease creep up her spine.

She pressed the intercom. 'Yes?'

The man turned. His head was dipped, whether to shelter him from the wind or the harsh security light, or to prevent identification, she wasn't sure.

'Delivery.'

'Can you just leave it?'

'Sorry. It'll get damaged, and I need a signature.' Not a local accent. English. Southern. Maybe London or Essex.

Shona's finger hovered over the latch button. 'Wait,' she said. 'I'll come out.'

The fencing was robust and high, the top covered by a line of anti-climb spikes. She'd have time to escape back to the house if he tried to force his way into the tarmacked area.

She could just see him through a crack between the gate and the post.

'Step back, please,' she ordered and then opened the gate a fraction, keeping the strong retainer chain on.

'Can you sign this please, love?' He passed a docket through, then indicated a tall, plastic-wrapped box. 'Thanks. I'll leave you to it.'

When he'd driven away, she cautiously opened the gate. The box was lighter than she expected. A slit handle on each side enabled her to carry it into the house. In the utility, she cautiously ran a knife around the wrapping and opened it at the marked lines.

An arc of beautiful, long-stemmed white roses sprang from their wrapping, which showed the logo of an upmarket florist in Glasgow's West End. Shona opened the attached card just as Becca came in from the kitchen, carrying two breakfast bowls.

Becca's eyes widened. 'Who are they from?'

'James McGowan,' Shona said flatly, reading the card. How on earth had he known where to send them? It was probably an assistant. Someone at the production company must know she ran a publicly listed B&B. It wouldn't have been that hard to look up her address.

'Wow, you must have made an impression yesterday.'

'Oh, I think it was more the other way around.' She handed Becca the note.

'"*Sorry for being such a dick.*" Okay, not your most conventional Hollywood autograph. I'm guessing your meeting didn't go as planned?'

'It didn't go at all,' Shona said. 'He refused to come out of the eighteenth century. Something about staying in character as the authentic Burns.'

'So did he remember you from school?'

Shona placed the flowers, complete with the accompanying crystal vase, on top of the washing machine, and shook her head.

'No reason he would have. It was years ago.'

Becca took down a plastic container of muesli from the cupboard.

'Mum, I've seen that school photo. You don't look any different,' she said with a sly smile.

She'd been Shona Mackenzie then, just another kid off the scheme. No ma or da. She had enough self-knowledge to know it was part of the reason she was fighting so hard now to keep her own family together.

'Does he look the same?'

'He looks like someone stuck a bicycle pump up his backside and inflated him.'

'Mum!' Becca snorted laughter and fake outrage. 'Those muscles are famous. He's done all those action films. Millions of women fancy him. They totally crush on him.' Becca held out a bowl to her mother.

'I met some of them yesterday,' Shona said, grimacing. 'But millions? Really?'

As she took the cereal from Becca, she remembered James McGowan at school, short and weedy, but funny and with a certain charm which had apparently deserted him in adulthood. He was Jazza, never James. He'd signalled an early inclination to swim against the tide and supported his mother's Edinburgh football team, Heart of Midlothian, which gave him his other nickname, Heartsy. Rangers-supporting pupils formed the bulk of the school population and, although Hearts were also a nominally Protestant team, this was offset by the rivalry between the two cities and not sufficient protection to excuse him the occasional kicking. It had positioned him both as an insider and an outsider, but it was probably his antics as the class clown that had seen him through.

'Weedy and gobby,' Shona concluded, knowing her opinion was coloured by yesterday's encounter. She followed Becca back into the kitchen. 'That's what I remember.' He had a reputation for talking back to teachers. Issues with authority was how it might be classed these days. She'd had a crush on him, and reasons to believe he liked her too. There'd been a school disco, a kiss. But now she could only look back on those times with a feeling akin to grief. The Jazza she'd believed she was in love with was dead, if he'd ever existed at all.

'Sit down, Mum. I'll make you some coffee. You look a bit peely-wally.' Becca took occasional delight in the Scots expressions she'd acquired since the move from London. It made her speech and accent a curious mixture.

Shona smiled. She probably did look pale, despite liberal bruise-concealing make-up. She was about to reply that she was fine, when she suddenly noticed Becca was dressed not in her pyjamas and hoodie, but in jeans and a thick jumper. Her daughter saw the questioning expression.

'I've got that work as an extra on the film,' Becca said quickly, making an ineffectual effort to hide her glee. 'I knew you wouldn't have time to ask, so I applied through the web. I've done the rooms for the next guests, that birdwatching couple. They can self check-in with the lockboxes.'

The birdwatchers were a last-minute booking via the B&B owners' group, after illness had forced the original host to cancel. They'd wanted full board, but reluctantly agreed to settle for self-catering. Shona had hoped to welcome them personally and make sure they had a positive experience, which would translate into a good review.

She could see Becca was shaping up for a battle. She'd have a convincing argument set out, but Shona wasn't about to argue. On balance, she realised, she'd rather have Becca with her on an island surrounded by the film's security cordon than alone at High Pines, well-defended though it was.

'Okay,' Shona said. 'You can come with me on Tommy's boat.'

'Really?' Becca blinked her surprise as she set the coffee mugs on the table.

'Absolutely.'

'Good, then I can make sure you're not overdoing it.' Becca grinned. 'Keep an eye on you.'

Same, Shona thought, but didn't say.

'Maybe I could interview James McGowan as Burns for my essay,' Becca said, chewing her cereal.

'Not on your nelly.' Shona remembered the scene with the young barmaid yesterday. 'I'm tellin' you, you won't like him. McGowan's concept of personal space around women is just as ancient as Burns's was. If he treated you like that, I'd have to arrest him on the spot. Either that, or he'd suddenly become even more authentically like Robert Burns.'

'How do you mean?' Becca frowned.

'He'd be dead.'

When Shona and Becca arrived at the pontoon in front of Kirkness RNLI station, the remaining film crew and kit were already there. The *Silver Crest* was a thirty-foot former fishing vessel built of larch over an oak frame by Tommy's father, half a century before. The hold had been adapted into a seven-berth cabin with a small galley. The boat's navigation lights and portholes shone against the blackness of the estuary, beacons of warmth in the raw winter morning.

Tommy and Becca banned Shona from lifting any heavy kit, so she went below and set a kettle on the gimballed stove. It would take about an hour to motor out to the island. They'd need hot drinks. From the porthole she could see the damaged yacht, *Ramsey Ranger*, still on a mooring buoy awaiting repair, but there was no sign of the Manxman, Larry Smith.

Once everyone was aboard, Tommy's partner, Freya, wrapped up in a pink anorak, thick wool hat and gloves, locked up the boatyard door and waved them off. Freya hailed from Orkney and a family of shipwrights, but not even a glimpse of Hollywood could coax her out onto the water this morning. Usefully for Shona, she'd agreed to act as a point of contact for the arriving High Pines guests if they had any problems.

Shona made sure everyone's lifejackets were secure while Becca joined Tommy in the wheelhouse. Over the sound of the boat's engine, Shona heard her daughter's excited chatter and Tommy's grunted replies. The two men and two women from the film crew, along with twenty or so metal cases and bags, were packed into the cabin. They were all suitably dressed for the trip, in warm clothes and waterproofs, likely their standard workwear given their careers. She handed each of them a wax paper bag.

'It'll be a bit rough once we get out past the headland, but don't worry, it's not far.' She smiled reassuringly. 'The aft deck is quite sheltered, if you need a breath of air, but please keep away from the rail. We don't want to be fishing you out of the Solway.'

Three of the four looked, if not happy, then at least resigned. But the older of the two men, in his forties and with thinning fair hair, was already far from relaxed. Shona brewed tea and offered biscuits, bracing herself against the galley countertop as the *Silver Crest* began to roll. She sat down next to the queasy-looking man, introduced herself and fished a packet of Kwells seasickness tablets from her pocket.

He shook his head. 'I'm already on double the dose.' He gave her a weak smile.

Barry Perkins turned out to be a London-based writer, responsible for the original screenplay, and part of the Boat Hoose Production company, rather than freelance crew. He was on hand to work through any necessary amendments to the script.

'So how much of this movie is based on the real life of Robert Burns?' she asked, trying to minimise the scepticism in her voice. Shona had often found that keeping a casualty focused on something other than their seasickness was the best way to stave it off.

'I know it reads like an action thriller at times.' He smiled. 'But Burns was an excise officer – he really did storm a smugglers' brig. It's in the historic record. He led a party of marines, pistol in hand. In those days excise officers were entitled to half the sale price of the recovered cargo and a bounty for every convicted smuggler, so it wasn't just for king and country.'

'What about this morning's scene?' All Shona knew about it was the single line on the sheet which said Burns was lured to the coast by a tip-off and a friend was captured by a smuggling gang.

'A little more artistic licence with this one. Burns and his colleague John Syme meet an informant on the beach but are double-crossed and Syme is taken hostage. If Burns turns a blind eye to the smugglers, Syme will be freed. He has to decide how best to save his friend.' Barry screwed up his face and took a sip of tea. 'We want to reflect the challenges he'd have faced in a way modern audiences will understand. Burns was responsible for collecting excise duty on things like spirits, wines, tea and tobacco. It was dangerous work. He went everywhere armed with a pair of double-barrelled flintlock pistols. His position would have made him a target for threats, bribes and blackmail.'

'I suppose it must,' Shona replied. The goods might have changed, but smugglers' methods hadn't. 'So... a bit different from the Robert Burns we see on shortbread tins?'

Barry gave a wry smile. 'It's easy to forget that Burns was a man of strong moral conscience, always pulled between his government job and his radicalism. Got himself in all sorts of bother over it. It's set in 1792: it was the Reign of Terror in France, and Britain had lost the Americas to revolutionaries. His position as a government employee required him to support King George III and the official line, but we know he wrote in a letter to a friend, Mrs Dunlop, *what my private sentiments are, you will find without an interpreter.*'

'But how do you work without a script?' Shona said, offering a biscuit, which Barry refused with a wave of his hand. He was looking increasingly pale and sweaty.

'My job is to help James tap into whatever emotion the scene requires,' he said.

Jeezo, thought Shona, there's a thankless task. Whatever they were paying this guy, it wasn't enough.

'The rest of the actors have their lines,' Barry continued, 'and they've rehearsed together for weeks, with a stand-in playing Burns. The trick is to build a meticulous but flexible structure. Occasionally, we need to rewrite the other parts as we go, so actions have consequences. The goal is improvised realism. Film-makers like Mike Leigh or Martin Scorsese use improvisation to a more or lesser extent. It's the most accurate way to get under the skin of life. Oh…'

'What?' Shona said, then quickly realised her efforts to distract Barry had been in vain as he retched noisily into the paper bag. The three other film crew, now green to the gills themselves, looked away.

'I'll just check how much further,' Shona said, and patted Barry's shoulder.

She climbed the steps into the wheelhouse. Becca had both hands clamped over her nose and mouth, and for a moment Shona though she too was feeling the effects of the rough crossing.

A second later she realised it wasn't seasickness, but an expression of horror.

'What is it?' Shona said. 'Tommy, what's the matter?'

'I was just aboot tae call you. Think we've got a wee problem.'

He pointed out, beyond the boat's bow. In the pearly, pre-dawn light, the dark bulk of Hildan Island loomed ahead, their landing spot at Holywell Bay still in deep shadow. Then Shona saw them. On the surface of the greasy grey sea lay flocks of small, soot-streaked clouds. As she looked closer, she realised what they were. Not clouds, but a scene of biblical devastation, and the bodies of hundreds upon hundreds of dead birds.

Chapter 9

Tommy reported the dead birds – which he identified as some of the huge numbers of barnacle geese which regularly overwintered on the Solway – to the coastguard. Shona went back down to the cabin, where she picked out the blonde woman, Maeve, a production assistant who, she knew, had a VHF radio linked to the main team in Hildan House.

'Tell everyone to stay away from the beach,' Shona instructed.

Maeve turned from the cabin porthole and held up the crackling radio. 'The second unit have just been on,' she said in her soft Donegal accent. 'There are loads of bird corpses on the sand, too. What's happened?'

'We don't know yet, but everyone needs to stay back until we do. The coastguard will be here shortly.' She looked across at Barry. 'Sorry, pal. We'll get you ashore soon as we can.'

Barry was fumbling with his phone, but Shona had already checked hers. There was no signal on this side of the island.

'Shit,' Barry said. 'We're on a really tight schedule. Is there no way we can do this?'

Shona shook her head. 'Not until we know what's happened.'

'What killed the birds, d'you think?' Maeve said.

'Could be a toxin like botulism… or a disease that's communicable to humans, like salmonellosis, some forms of encephalitis or avian tuberculosis.'

Shona's remit at Dumfries CID covered wildlife crime, so mass bird-kills was something she'd been briefed on. Causes ranged from poisonings and disease, to fireworks, lightning or even high-altitude hailstorms. They weren't that far from Kilcatrin, an MOD firing range, whose environmental record included lobbing depleted uranium shells into the Solway. Whatever it was that had caused this horrific event, she wasn't taking any chances.

Tommy came down the first step from the wheelhouse and with a tilt of the head beckoned Shona to follow him back up. Becca sat in the corner seat, hugging her legs, which were drawn up in front of her, and biting her bottom lip. Shona reached out and ran her hand once across her daughter's hair. *Okay?* she mouthed. Becca gave her the smallest of nods.

On the far horizon, Shona saw that a coastguard patrol vessel was approaching.

'They're bringing the RSPB warden o'er from Merse-head,' Tommy said. 'So far, the dead birds seem to be confined to the east side of Hildan. Nae reports fae else-where yet. What d'you want to do about yon film folk?'

The plan had been to ferry these crew members ashore directly to the scene location in Holywell Bay using the fishing boat's small tender.

'Can you take us to the other side of the island? Put us down at Hildan House?' Shona said. 'I'll talk to the director and Dumfries police control room. See what we can sort out.'

'Nae bother,' Tommy replied. He restarted the engine and began easing the *Silver Crest* slowly back from the bay.

They left the sandy cove behind, passing tall cliffs and rounding the point to where woods sprang up around the more sheltered eastern side of the island. The mood aboard the old fishing boat was sombre. Death on such a scale was sobering.

In the growing light, the lichen-covered roof of Hildan House was just visible among the bare, blackened fingers of the winter trees. In front was a short stone jetty. Shona went to the bow of the *Silver Crest* and threw a mooring line to a waiting film technician, then she stepped ashore and secured the stern to a second iron ring.

As Becca and Tommy helped the others from the fishing boat, Shona was relieved to see she had a signal: she called Dumfries police command to report she was at the locus and confirm what the coastguard had relayed to them. Bird wardens would already be checking the mainland shore, but they needed to get a warning out to the public not to touch any dead birds they found.

The party moved up the unmade track to the main house, through a plantation of oak and birch saplings, their trunks muted grey pencil lines above the faded wisps of dead winter grasses.

The bones of Hildan House were ancient. The building dated back to the early monastic settlement of St Hilda's that had given the island its name. Stone lintels, carved here and there with strange marks, braced the doors. The small windows, white-framed against the grey granite, had leaded upper panes giving the appearance of narrowed eyes in a squared-off face. The open double doors of the main entrance, with their flaking red paint, looked like a wide mouth, shrieking in horror, and it took Shona a moment to realise the unhappy sound was not coming from the building itself but human voices within.

'It's them. I'm fuckin' telling you, it's them. It's the fuckin' AG!'

James McGowan stood red-faced in the entrance hall amid oak panelling, heavy dark furniture and a fireplace large enough to park a truck in. His Robert Burns costume was absent, replaced by black jeans, T-shirt and biker boots. Hands on his hips, he paced the flagstones then returned to jab a finger in his director's face.

'You were supposed to fix this. It's deliberate.'

Simon Jones held up placating hands. 'Look, James, we don't know that.'

Shona left the others, who stayed warily by the entrance, and crossed to the two men. The remaining principal cast, crew and extras, who'd been squeezed into the house overnight on camp beds, were conspicuous by their absence. All the new arrivals, except Barry the script editor, followed their lead and beat a hasty retreat out the front door.

'What d'you mean, "deliberate"?' Shona said. 'Is this about the dead birds?'

'Tell her,' James ordered the director then strode across to brace his hands against the mantle above the fireplace as if he was holding up the structure on his own. Shona saw the muscles of his back flex beneath the tight T-shirt as he stared at the dull embers of the smouldering logs in the grate.

'Umm, last year…' Simon began. 'We made a film in the Arctic. Cash was tight. At the last minute a company called Northgoose stepped in with cold-weather clothes for the cast and crew. James was photographed wearing one of their jackets. Soon after, the company was implicated in a scandal over their use of fur trims, wild animal trapping and inhumane killing of huge numbers of birds for their clothes. An environmentalist group, the Arctic Guardians, started targeting James. Bryson Drake, James's agent—'

'Ex-agent,' McGowan cut in.

'His *ex-agent*,' Simon corrected himself. 'Well, he was supposed to fix it. The production company have issued rebuttals to the claims James was promoting the brand, but, well...' He spread his hands to indicate that Shona could see for herself how successful that had been.

'I've been a vegetarian for years, for fuck's sake,' James said. 'I'm the gift that just keeps on giving for these folk. The picture of me in that bastard jacket just keeps circling the bowl like the unflushable shit it is.'

'Everyone's on edge,' Simon said. 'Filming's already been delayed by legal problems with Bryson, security issues with over-zealous fans and precarious funding.'

'And you think the dead birds are the action of this group, Arctic Guardians?' Shona said.

'Course it's them.' James pushed off from the fire-place and spun to face her. He seemed to swell, bristling with anger. She could almost smell the testosterone reek off him. Instead of taking a step back, she squared her shoulders and held her ground.

'Based on what evidence?' she said.

'Based on more bad fuckin' publicity for me when this hits the press. Also, wrecking our filming schedule. We could fuckin' fold if we get any further behind.'

McGowan suddenly seemed to notice Becca, who was leaning against an oak dresser, scrolling through her phone.

'You filming this?' he barked. 'You better not be.'

Becca glanced up. 'I'm checking the socials.'

'Am I trending?' McGowan asked anxiously.

'No,' Becca replied, her expression a masterwork of withering teenage disdain.

Shona almost applauded. It was what he deserved. *Sorry for being such a dick*, the card with the flowers had said. Not sorry enough, it seemed, to mend his ways.

Tommy McCall, who'd been watching the exchange with a deepening frown, stepped forward. He took James McGowan's arm firmly, shocking the actor into momentary silence, and drew him away from the others. Shona saw Tommy say something into James's ear that caused the actor's expression to change from rage to one of flushed embarrassment. After a few moments, he locked eyes with the older man and nodded a few times, before turning back to Simon Jones and touching the director's arm.

'Sorry, pal.' He looked to Shona and Becca. 'Sorry, ladies.'

The director looked more startled at this turn of events than the disaster unfolding in the firth.

'Could the geese have been poisoned?' Shona said to Tommy, keen to take advantage of McGowan's unexpected change in mood. The dead birds might not have hit social media yet, but it didn't mean they wouldn't. She couldn't believe an environmentalist group would deliberately kill geese but then she'd seen renegade hunt saboteurs spray mace in the faces of foxhounds and strew nails in the paths of horses to make their point.

'They could have been poisoned,' Tommy admitted. 'Geese get pretty hungry this time o' year. Wouldnae be hard to lure them with grain laced wi' somethin'. Farmers used to do it tae stop the birds competing for winter grazing an' fouling the merse wi' droppings that infected livestock.'

'You think that's what happened here?' Simon asked, exchanging a concerned glance, mingled with guilty hope, with James.

'Mibbaes,' Tommy replied. 'But more likely it's bird flu. There's been significant mortality in wild birds fae Shetland, right doon the Western Isles, and intae the Solway this winter.'

Shona nodded. She'd seen the briefing notes, and the possibility had already crossed her mind. She just hadn't been prepared for the sheer scale of it. Thousands of birds in a single swoop.

'We'll know if that's the case, once the birds are tested,' she said.

'And we can shoot at Holywell Bay after the birds are cleared?' Simon asked.

Shona nodded. 'If it is bird flu, there's less risk of transmission of the virus to humans in an open environment, although you shouldn't touch dead or ill birds yourselves.'

McGowan had been watching this exchange silently, his eyes mostly on Tommy McCall. 'How long will the clean-up take?' he asked.

'Couple of days,' Shona said and waited for the explosion.

McGowan's mouth set in a hard line, but when he spoke, it was to Tommy. 'You know this area. The island, the tides. Could you have a wee look at the map, maybe suggest an alternative spot?'

'Aye, course,' Tommy said. 'What d'you need?'

McGowan led Tommy, Simon Jones and Barry through into a side room filled with leather armchairs and dark wood furniture, where a map of the island was pinned to the wall.

When the others had gone, Shona turned to Becca. 'You weren't recording that, were you?'

'No, but maybe I should have. All the toys out of the pram, or what!' she said, grabbing her mother's arm, doubling up with suppressed laughter. 'He's gonna need a florist on speed dial to stop you slapping the handcuffs on him before the end of this film.'

'I might have done it now if Tommy hadn't stepped in,' Shona replied, grimly. 'Not a word about this to anyone, mind?'

Becca mimed zipping her mouth shut. 'Saving it for my memoir. Be a best-seller at this rate.'

Two minutes later, the others were back. An alternative location for the scene had been decided on, subject to a check by Tommy and Shona for any dead birds.

'I'll need to have a chat with your set security,' Shona said. 'Where are they?'

McGowan exchanged a glance with Barry and Simon Jones. 'Gone. Didn't think we'd need them on the island. Cost-cutting.' McGowan's final look at the two other members of Boat Hoose Productions made it clear that while it had been a group decision, he was holding them responsible now events had taken a downturn.

'Mr McGowan,' Shona began, 'you must remain vigilant about your personal safety.'

He gave her a curt nod of agreement.

'Recall your set security. It's false economy if an issue they could have prevented results in an undesirable outcome. And you need to stay at Hildan House until they arrive.'

'Not possible,' he said. 'Can't lose a day's shooting. Anyway, we've got you.'

'I'm here purely as a courtesy.' Shona bristled. 'My job is to assist, where possible, to ensure the smooth running of your operation. I'm not your bodyguard. I can only advise you.'

'And I totally respect your advice,' McGowan responded.

'But you're not willing to take it?'

Shona and McGowan eyeballed each other. She thought he was studying her almost-healed black eye and felt suddenly self-conscious, before chiding herself that such an unattractive feature hardly mattered. He was talking to her the way he used to confront the teachers at school. But now, as an adult, she no longer found it either funny or impressive. She wasn't having it. Tommy stood to the side with his arms folded. This was Shona's area of expertise, and she knew he wouldn't step in a second time. It was Simon Jones who broke the impasse.

'We'll abide by any recommendations you have, DI Oliver,' he said, formally, deferring to her judgement. 'We can minimise the time James is required on set, until security get here and we know what happened to the birds.'

McGowan stood with folded arms, regarding her.

Shona consulted her watch. The set security company would be here before dark.

'And you'll call me the minute there's any issues,' she said.

He gave the barest of nods, then turned and left the hallway.

Simon flashed her an apologetic smile then followed the actor.

Despite arguing with her, one thing was clear: McGowan believed the threat to himself and the production amounted to more than just a few crazy fans.

'What did you say to McGowan?' Shona asked Tommy as they made their way back to the *Silver Crest*.

'Aye, well, I told him to pipe down,' Tommy replied. 'If he's the boss, he needs tae show leadership. Fix the problem. Have respect for his crew if he wants them tae respect him.'

'Wouldn't argue with that,' Shona said. She'd been surprised McGowan had taken it quite so well. She'd once read something about how men will only defer to other men of equal or higher status than themselves. As lifeboat helm, Tommy was a natural figure of authority, and it seemed that influence stretched well beyond the yellow wellies.

'He needs tae get a grip on thon temper,' Tommy mused. 'But he looks a fit lad.'

'You're not thinking of recruiting him for the lifeboat, are you?' Shona grinned.

'I suppose Hollywood's a bit far for a shout.' Tommy's lined face cracked into a wide smile. 'Pity.'

'Maybe you should be doing the liaison on the film. Persuading James McGowan not to lose the heid on a regular basis would probably make my life a damn sight easier.'

'I've seen you take on worse.' Tommy gave her a wink. 'Nae contest. Almost feel sorry for the lad.'

Shona smiled at Tommy's vote of confidence and prayed that, with everything else she had on her plate at the minute, he was right.

Chapter 10

To the west of the stone pier, the shoreline rose once more to steep cliffs. Rigid plates of rock leaned against the land like vast ancient volumes, their bindings blackened by the sea. In other places, the rock layers folded back on themselves like the serpentine track of some long-vanished sea monster. Known locally as the Captain's Eye, a great sea arch – the base of which was accessible only for a few hours on either side of low tide – towered above them. It was reputed to be haunted by a smuggler who'd refused to leave his sinking ship as it was driven onto this unforgiving shore, and who returned each full moon to urge unwary travellers to follow him into the ghostly storm.

The director of photography, Jan – a Dutchman in waterproof salopettes and boots – arrived. He tugged on his bushy, blonde moustache, considering, then pronounced this far superior to the original location. They would shoot through the arch, Jan decided, the rock framing the action with a heavy sense of foreboding.

So, she wasn't the only one who felt the menacing atmosphere. The tall cliffs shut out the sky. Whole tree trunks of driftwood were scattered among the brash of seaweed like dinosaur bones. Cockles lay on the beach, their shells open like pairs of pleading hands. No birds sang, but two crows hung on the wind, watching. Shona shivered. Perhaps that was why the bay had been used by smugglers: the ill-favoured atmosphere kept inquisitive locals away. Similar tales attached to other smuggling haunts on the Dumfries and Galloway coast: siren-like witches, long-dead monks and ghostly pipers.

The dozen modern-day brigands were waiting a little way back from the shore, foil blankets over their eighteenth-century garb. Cheerful, despite the cold weather and the delays, they presented a full range of smuggling types: a painfully thin young woman with straggly blonde hair, a man with one arm and two stocky balding men. There was also an athletic-looking older woman with long, white hair who transformed herself into a bent and aged crone when required. Shona saw her daughter, in a full-length skirt and shawl, talking with a stooped man whose white costume beard hid most of his face.

Becca turned and waved, revealing a gap-toothed smile. 'Hi, Mum.'

Shona realised with a start that one of Becca's front teeth had been blacked out by the make-up department. While heartily disapproving of this disfigurement of her beautiful girl, Shona had to admit Becca looked like she was enjoying herself – she hoped it would mitigate some of the unpleasant memories of earlier that morning.

Tommy also looked to be in his element, standing at the water's edge with Simon Jones and Jan the Dutchman, pointing out to the firth in a way that made Shona think they must be discussing the state of the tide. She'd been hoping for an update from the RSPB warden or Dumfries control room but when she checked her phone, there was no signal.

When everyone was finally ready, James arrived, all swirling greatcoat, breeches and tall boots – Robert Burns once more.

At least Shona didn't have to worry about Lilly Chase: the actress wasn't needed for this scene and remained at Hildan House, with her own security. The move to the island should have made the set more secure but it seemed that the threat was more complicated. Shona kept an eye on the background artists, in case one of the activists had slipped in. She also scanned the sea for any suspicious boats. She could just imagine an environmental activist group like the Arctic Guardians motoring into shot, banner unfurled, with a news crew in tow. Never mind McGowan, it was not the kind of press coverage the area needed. The tourist industry, her small part in it included, could do without that sort of publicity.

'Feeling better?' she asked Barry the scriptwriter, whom she'd joined in the rough scrub above the tideline, well out of shot.

He gave her a weak smile. 'Sorry about earlier.'

'Happens to the best of us.'

'I lasted one day on a canal boat holiday,' Barry replied. 'My girlfriend chucked me.'

'Ah, okay.' Shona gave him a sympathetic smile.

'Anyway, you think you could hit me over the head with a rock? Knock me unconscious for the return journey?'

'I guarantee that wouldn't make you feel any better, and probably a lot worse,' Shona said with conviction.

There were shouts from below for quiet. McGowan as Burns, and the other man she'd seen him with his arm around in the pub yesterday, strode forward. The film's armourer, listed in the paperwork as Sven Wales from Celtic Custom Armoury – a gaunt man in his fifties with a high ponytail and trim beard – handed Burns his double-barrelled flintlock pistols. Sven's daughter Caris, who worked as his assistant, fitted each of the actors with a belted scabbard containing a long sword with brass handle guards.

McGowan's companion drew his blade and slashed expertly at the air around him, the sword flexing and flashing like quicksilver in the dull air. Then both walked purposefully towards Jan and the camera team. Shona waited until someone called *cut* and turned back to Barry.

'Who is this with Burns?'

'John Syme, son of the Laird of Barncailzie. He was a former army captain who managed his father's estate, but a bank collapse forced him to find other work collecting stamp duty. That's how he met Burns. You probably recognise the actor? Michael Vincent?' Shona looked blank. 'You know,' Barry continued, 'Inspector Baker off *Baker Street*. The Sherlock Holmes modern reboot? Huge hit.'

She scrutinised the tall, fair-haired man whose curls were artfully gathered into a beribboned ponytail. Noticing her gaze, he shot her a brief red-carpet smile as if her attention was nothing more than his due.

'Sorry,' Shona said, aware she must be a grave disappointment to Barry.

'I guess cops don't watch cop shows.' He grinned.

'Not generally. But his face does look familiar.'

'Perhaps you arrested him?' Barry said, lowering his voice. 'Bit of a bad boy, if you know what I mean.'

Shona raised her eyebrows enquiringly. 'Drugs?'

'Let's just say his US visa is in jeopardy,' Barry said, then shifted uneasily. 'He may be facing a MeToo moment as well. His agent's keen to get him work here while he sorts himself out. We're taking a risk casting him. Investors are jumpy about any scandal. But he's box-office gold, and James wants to give him the chance. They're old friends.'

There was another call for silence. Shona watched as the smuggling gang surged forward, Becca among them, and tried not to wince as she saw blades drawn on both sides. One of the smugglers held a gun to John Syme's head, forcing Burns to halt as his friend was dragged away. She jumped as Burns fired his pistol twice in quick succession, the sound ricocheting of the cliffs. The ringing in her ears subsided to the panicked calls of the crows that flew upwards like two soaring flakes of ash as smoke engulfed the scene.

Barry put a hand on her arm and smiled. 'It's perfectly safe. No live ammunition allowed on set.'

'I should hope so,' Shona said, her heart pounding. 'This is way more embarrassing than your seasickness, I assure you.'

'Why?' Barry said, puzzled.

'I'm an AFO,' she said with a self-deprecating smile. 'Authorised firearms officer.'

Barry laughed.

Shona strained to identify Becca in the melee and was rewarded by a glimpse of her daughter punching the air in delight. Shona was also reassured to see the armourer retrieve and check the weapons. Whatever her mother's fears, Becca didn't share them and ran back along the beach, giggling with another girl.

'So, the smugglers take John Syme hostage,' Shona said, 'in order to blackmail Burns into turning a blind eye to their activities?'

'That's right,' Barry replied.

'Why doesn't Burns just tell his bosses at the Excise?'

'Both men are motivated by the reward for catching the smugglers. Syme also has gambling debts, so it's financial. For Burns it's more complicated. A cock-up in which the son of the Laird of Barncailzie is captured would end his career. The smugglers will claim he's in on the kidnap. This was just what his enemies needed to see him dancing on the end of a rope. Burns believed a fair few excise officers were corrupt. He didn't know who to trust. He needs to rescue Syme on his own.'

'So is it a case of art imitating life?' Shona said. 'James sticking his neck out to rescue Michael Vincent.'

'I suppose it is.' Barry smiled, then his expression turned serious. 'But let's hope it's not a facsimile.'

'Why not?'

'Because for all Burns does for Syme, he's ultimately betrayed by him.'

'How?'

'It's a set-up. Syme is part of the smuggling gang. Loyalty is one of the central themes of the film. Loyalty to your family, to your friends, to your job, to your country. They're all tensions Burns encountered, and we think also something everyone faces at some point in their lives. How far would you go to save your family or your friends? It's one of the ways we hope to connect with the audience.'

Shona pondered this as she watched the camera crew setting up for a new angle. Beneath the great arch of the Captain's Eye, McGowan and Michael Vincent were clearly easy in each other's company, brothers in arms. Loyalty to your fellow actors was one thing, but Vincent's troubles with the law could only add to McGowan's public image problems. Some people didn't deserve the trust placed in them. She'd seen that a hundred times over.

Shona scanned the firth again for any sign of activists, then turned to scrutinise the remaining cast and crew. Becca aside, any one of them could pose a threat. She thought of the easy way in which her daughter gained access to the set.

'Barry,' she said, 'how does Boat Hoose recruit its extras?'

'Some are professional background artists. They travel all over in their camper vans. Some come through local acting groups, others via an agency. There's an app you can use.'

Perhaps it was the lingering toll from this morning's scene of mass death, or the sudden influx of people into a place so obviously made for isolation, but the air of deep unease Shona felt when she'd first arrived hadn't dissipated. She'd never normally have reacted to the noise of the pistols like that. Since Rob's attack, and the potential dropping of Delfont's case, a perpetual edginess had taken hold. They were on an uninhabited island surrounded by the moat of the Solway, so Delfont or the gang behind the money laundering couldn't touch her and her daughter here. But as she looked up at the great stone arch, she had the nagging sensation that there were eyes on her that didn't just belong to the long-vanished captain.

Chapter 11

While the crew broke up for lunch and a scene reset, Shona walked back to the stone jetty. The wind had vanished. Ripples of low cloud were distinguishable above a thin mist. Far over to the west, and although it was barely afternoon, the sky had a sulphur tinge of sunset and the coming night.

As soon as her phone latched onto a signal, updates from the coastguard arrived. They'd begun to recover the dead birds. A sample was on its way to the lab in Glasgow. The results would take them a step closer to the likely cause of the bird-kill event, and might even be available as soon as tomorrow. As yet, there was no indication it was a deliberate act by an environmental protest group, as McGowan had feared.

Shona had decided not to pass the potential threat from the Arctic Guardians up the line to her Super. Without credible information, it would be difficult to act. McGowan's belief that he was being targeted was much stronger than the current evidence suggested, but she couldn't ignore it completely.

There was no news from Murdo on the whereabouts of the fatal fire suspect, Joe Dylan, birth father of Taylor and convicted arsonist. She was itching to call DI Dalrymple for an update, but if he felt she was stepping on his toes, it would go straight back to the Super. Murdo was right, better to keep Davies sweet. She didn't have the energy at the minute to open a war on another front. Instead, she selected DC Kate Irving's number.

'Everything okay, Kate? Did the file go off to the fiscal on that serious assault?'

'Yes, boss. The brother didn't deny it. In his view, it was family, not police business if he chose to batter his wee brother. I've flagged it to Inter-agency Adult Support. It might be a safeguarding issue. The fiscal's happy to proceed with what we've got.'

'That's good,' Shona said. 'Well done, Kate. Now, I need you to do some digging for me on James McGowan. Has he ever been in bother with the police, here or in the US? I want to know of any potential threats to his person. There was a firearms incident recently with a disturbed fan in Hollywood. Find out who that individual was, and if they're in custody. If they're not, check they haven't decided Scotland in January's their must-see destination.'

'Yes, boss,' Kate said. 'Is there trouble?'

Shona told her about the possible bird poisoning, and McGowan potentially being targeted by the Arctic Guardians.

'I've just pulled up a page on that now,' Kate replied.

Shona could hear the buzz and chatter of the CID office in the background and suddenly had an immense longing to be out of this biting cold and back at her desk making decisions that would result in positive outcomes, instead of stuck on a freezing beach with a spoiled brat playing make-believe.

'Ooh, yes,' Kate said. 'See what you mean. AG and PETA had a go at him, then it was just your regular social media pile-on. Mind you, urgh, the photographs of coyotes in traps and goose slaughter are pretty horrific.'

'You should try seeing it in the flesh,' Shona said.

'Sorry, boss. Is it bad?'

Shona had witnessed some terrible sights – road accidents, murders, victims long dead. Most officers had. She wanted to say, *it's just birds*, but somehow that didn't come near the scale of what she'd experienced that morning.

'It's going to take a bit of clearing up,' she replied. 'Can you also look at Michael Vincent for me? He's one of the actors.'

'Oh, I know who he is,' Kate said with enthusiasm. 'Inspector Baker of *Baker Street*.'

'It's his factual connections with the law I'm interested in.'

'Okay, I'll check it out. What about Lilly Chase?'

Shona considered for a moment, then said, 'Lilly is the most clued-up about personal security, and she didn't raise any potential threats beyond over-enthusiastic fans – we can leave her to her own team. Listen, Kate, thanks for this. Signal's patchy here. I'll give you a call tomorrow.'

'One more thing, boss. Just to let you know, Sean Nicolson died this morning.'

Shona felt for Sonya Nicolson. The loss of half her family was something she might never recover from, and the thought that Taylor's father might be behind it must be torture.

'Any sign of Joe Dylan?'

'Not yet,' Kate replied with a sigh, which Shona refrained from interpreting as anything other than empathy for the family, and definitely not dissatisfaction at the new SIO. 'But Dylan has previous for harassing the family, and he threatened the neighbours too. Seems that's why they were cagey on the door-to-door, not because of any parking dispute. They were just worried Dylan would target them too. But it's looking more likely by the minute that Dylan's gone to ground.'

Shona wished Kate luck and ended the call. There was her update after all, but it wasn't the one she was hoping for. She opened her contact number for Sonya Nicolson and considered calling to express her condolences. The woman would, quite rightly, have questions about the investigation. What could Shona tell her? Plenty of platitudes. Is this what she'd come to? A foray into grief tourism designed to make herself feel she was of practical use. She swiped the page away.

Tommy appeared at the top of the track leading to the house. He waved, then mimed eating a sandwich to ask if she was coming in for some lunch. Shona indicated she'd be there shortly. She had no appetite. Film catering had brought portable hobs which ran on bottle gas, and were doing a herculean job keeping people fed. If she didn't eat now, the island offered no alternatives.

Her screen showed yesterday's four missed calls from an unknown London number. Whoever the caller was, they hadn't left a message. The CPS or the detectives on Operation Vita, the inquiry into the rape allegations against Delfont, would have contacted her from automatically withheld office numbers, so it was unlikely to be them.

The shock of finding the dead birds, and the business of the morning, had been a welcome distraction from the previous day's news about Rob and the possible collapse of the Delfont case. But only in the way you could be distracted from a large spider in the corner of the room. Even if you don't look at it directly, you're aware of its presence and the need, eventually, to tackle it.

Shona scrutinised the number. She had a hunch who the caller was, although they hadn't spoken since Shona had moved north. She pressed the redial button.

'Hi, Thalia,' Shona said, when the familiar voice answered.

Witnesses weren't supposed to contact each other before a trial. Shona didn't know the identities of the other two women who'd come forward with complaints against Delfont, but it didn't take a detective of her standing to work out they were likely to have served at her station. Thalia had obviously had the same thought.

Thalia Brookes had grown up in Brixton, her grandparents having arrived on the *Windrush* from Jamaica in 1948. Her grandfather was following his older brother, who'd been a wireless operator in the RAF and lost his life in the service of his country. Public service ran in the family.

When Shona had been in London giving her statement to the Met's investigation, she'd called Thalia at Bishopsgate, on the off chance her old colleague would be free for a drink, only to be told DS Brookes was off with 'stress'. Something in the constable's tone, rather than his words, had alerted Shona. Thalia had been a highly committed officer who'd never missed a day. As an off-duty rookie cop, she'd been at Canary Wharf, meeting a friend for a drink, in February 1996 when an IRA bomb had gone off just after seven p.m., plunging much of the complex into darkness. Thalia had received a commendation for her prompt treatment of an injured office worker, whose life she'd undoubtedly saved. Though injured herself, Thalia was back on duty the next morning.

It took only a moment for Thalia to confirm that what Rob's barrister had heard was true. The CPS were not proceeding with the charges against DCI Harry Delfont. Shona's lack of appetite grew into a tidal wave of nausea that threatened to engulf her. She crouched down, her free hand flat on the cold granite of the pier flagstones, to steady herself.

'I thought I was getting over it,' Thalia said. 'Then I had a case, recently. A young, deaf, Black woman manipulated into hiding drugs and weapons by the man she thought was her boyfriend, someone she thought she could trust. Classic cuckooing. When she tried to escape, he killed her.'

'That sort of job hits everyone hard,' Shona said. The deep breaths of the cold Solway air were helping to calm her, although she took care to stop short of the point where rib pain kicked in. 'There should have been support available.'

Thalia sighed. 'I know the cases are different, but I began to think, *she* didn't see it coming, but *I* should have. Delfont was always a manipulative scrote, looking for ways to get you in his debt. Picking up on minor stuff and making sure you knew you owed him for letting it slide. Making you his accomplice in minor infringements. How'd I miss the signs? I began to think, if I'd just done this, or that, none of the rest of it would have happened. Then I couldn't stop thinking that maybe, just maybe, what happened to me, to us, was in some tiny way my fault.'

Shona hadn't been immune to the same line of reasoning. If she'd evaded being targeted by Delfont, Rob wouldn't be in jail, their business facing ruin, and her job hanging by a thread. As soon as she thought this, she pushed it away. No one could change the past.

'You know it isn't your fault,' Shona said gently. 'If that victim was sitting in front of you now, what would you tell her? You'd say, *it's not your fault* and mean it.'

'I know I'm not the only one this happened to, and at least I'm still alive. I'm not a coward. I'd stand up in court and say what happened. So why does it keep playing over and over in my head?'

'Being a police officer doesn't make you immune. What happened to you, to both of us, was horrendous. He won't get away with it. There'll be an inquiry.'

'Professional standards will just charge him with something petty. A few forms and some hand-wringing, and it'll all get swept under the carpet. It was rape. He filmed it. How can what he did to us not be deemed a crime?'

'I know. But we're not the CPS. We just enforce the law as best we can in the circumstances, and yes, sometimes it isn't fit for purpose, but that's for the lawmakers to fix. We can't.'

'But it's not right.'

'I agree. But we both know the CPS won't pursue something that his defence will just bat away. They'll only proceed if they think they can get a conviction.' Shona paused. 'We need to find out why they changed their minds.'

'The CPS won't tell us.'

'What about Operation Vita? Do you know anyone there who might say, cop to cop, what happened?' Shona searched her memory. 'There was a DC Joyce Gillingham who took my statement.'

'Mine too,' Thalia said. 'Suppose I could call her.'

Shona could call DC Gillingham herself but, just at this moment, taking action would help Thalia to feel she was at least doing something. If they knew why they were being denied the chance of a conviction perhaps they'd be able to see a way forward.

Shona felt that it had grown darker even in the minutes she'd been standing there, on the edge of the stone jetty. The *Silver Crest* sat higher in the water, raised up by a returning tide that had brought not hope of renewal, but a dusting of fine black feathers, like the funeral ashes of the vanished flock.

'The bastard's got away with it,' Thalia said. To Shona, she sounded brittle and on edge.

'No,' Shona assured her, aware she was trying to convince herself as much as her friend. 'This isn't over. We'll get justice.'

'Justice,' Thalia replied, her tone mocking. 'I gave up believing in justice a long time ago.'

Chapter 12

For the rest of the afternoon, cloud thickened, eventually driving the crew to set up an interior scene, slated to appear near the beginning of the movie. Candles and oil lamps were set in niches until the main hall was a patchwork of buttery light and velvet shadows, as Robert Burns and his friend John Syme sat before the great hearth, tankards in hand. Their earnest faces were etched by firelight while they plotted to outsmart the fates and gain their fortunes.

Shona took a seat near the back of the set, glad to rest her aching ribs, whose pain had been exacerbated by the rough crossing and a morning of walking around uneven ground. The crew had retired to another room to discuss the camera placement, their presence a low murmur of voices. From outside came the faintest sound of waves over shingle. Inside, the scent of woodsmoke overlaid the last traces of the crew's cooked lunch. A few extras sat quietly at side tables, like figures in an oil painting.

'Beautiful, isn't it?' murmured a voice.

The background artist with the full white beard who had been talking to Becca was at her shoulder. He had a soft West Country accent at odds with the Scots of Dumfries and Galloway. Shona imagined he was one of the professional extras that Barry had mentioned, probably non-speaking. He certainly looked the part in a long leather jerkin over a filthy linen shirt, breeches and worn-out boots.

'Think you'd like to go back to them days?' His dark eyes twinkled in the candlelight. He was part-charm, part-menace — and a more convincing smuggler you couldn't hope to meet.

In her waterproof jacket and jeans, Shona suddenly felt uncomfortably out of place, an encroaching phantom from the future.

'I've never been nostalgic for any period that lacked effective policing, never mind antibiotics and safe child-birth.' Shona shook her head. 'Would you?'

'Appin I would,' he said, quietly. 'Can't help but wonder if you could alter things for the better. All of them unlived futures.'

If Shona was given a portal to the past, would she step through it?

His words put her in mind of the conversation earlier with Thalia Brookes. Thalia was torturing herself with the idea that she could, somehow, have prevented Delfont's attack on her and others. He'd drugged her as they worked late on an important case and assaulted her right there in her own office, where she was woken the next morning by her colleagues, who'd joked she shouldn't be a police officer if she kept falling asleep at her desk. Maybe she couldn't handle the pace. As a Black female detective, she had forged a path, facing down racism and misogyny, but the attack had destroyed her sense that justice was even possible. If Thalia was asked that question, Shona had no doubt she'd take the opportunity to go back. But what if you did, and nothing changed? Thinking like this was just another way of punishing yourself for being the victim of another's wrongdoing. Past or present, you weren't responsible for their evil deeds, and it wasn't your job to atone for them.

Shona was suddenly aware of the smuggler watching her, waiting for her answer.

'No one can change the past,' she said.

'True,' he replied. 'But, from time to time, we all like to think it possible, don't we, my luvver?' He gave her a wink followed by a smile of tombstone teeth, which Shona sincerely hoped were the work of the make-up department. She watched him limp back to his table, her mood now as dark as the shadows that seemed to be creeping from corners to swallow the last of the light.

The crew returned; shooting began. The enfolding gloom left Shona unnoticed at the back of the hall. She watched for a while then let herself drift, lulled by the heat from the fire, the far-off sound of the sea and the occasional crackle of burning logs. She tried to let her mind empty, trusting her experience to sift for treasures, like a beachcomber walking the shore, bending to retrieve an interesting object to be examined, then pocketed or discarded.

The briefing document, the shooting schedule, even her exchanges with cast and crew hadn't provided enough for her to work with. Maybe tomorrow, after her chat with DC Kate Irving, she'd have more to go on and the true nature of the threat would emerge like a polished gem from the sea of shingle.

Shona felt a hand on her arm. She opened her eyes. The candles had burned themselves out, the oak panelling of the otherwise empty room lit solely by the glow of embers in the great fireplace. Becca was smiling at her and, to Shona's relief, she appeared to have a full set of teeth once more. Shona sat up and rubbed her eyes.

'Are we off soon?' Becca asked. Shona wondered if the day on the cold beach had ended her daughter's enthusiasm for working as a film extra. Then she remembered that she'd promised Becca could talk to her father on the phone this evening.

'Tommy's ready to go,' Becca added.

Shona checked the time. Just before six p.m. The film company's plan for the evening was to keep everyone indoors. They'd go over the set arrangements for tomorrow until dinner, then have a social hour of board games and a quiz, and probably a bit of Robert Burns poetry, before packing people off to bed. To Shona's surprise, there was no alcohol on the island: the film's insurance specified a dry set to cut down on the chance of high jinks.

Shona got up and stretched. Security should be here by now. She'd check they were up to speed and then they could get going. The bird clean-up operation would be far from finished, suspended by the coastguard until first light, but she was glad for Becca's sake that they wouldn't have to witness the devastation again on the way home.

Heading up the firth once more, she looked forward as she always did to catching that first glimpse of Kirkness, a steep scattering of hillside lights against the pressing darkness of sea and night sky. Somewhere on that border stood the lighthouse form of High Pines, a beacon of all she held dear, drawing her home.

–

The next morning, Shona was up early. She'd slept well, and her priority was to make sure her birdwatching guests were happy and likely to leave a good review. The dead geese were all over the news, and she was ready with a list of inland options in the Galloway hills where raptors, including buzzards and red kites, could be spotted. In the end she needn't have worried. Freya had obviously informed the guests of Shona's role in alerting the coast-guard to the dead birds, which had elevated her to the status of wildlife warrior. The guests turned out to be experienced volunteers on Frampton Marsh reserve in Lincolnshire and wanted nothing more than to help with the clear-up, a point they made with a fervour bordering on the religious. Shona promised she'd call the bird warden at Mersehead reserve on their behalf, reflecting that – for the most perverse of reasons – a five-star review might just be in the bag.

Shona made her way back upstairs. As she passed Becca's room, she saw her daughter still asleep, a jumble of wavy brown hair visible above the tightly bunched duvet. Shona pulled the half-open door quietly closed.

Becca had spoken to her father on the phone the night before. Yes, he was fine. No, darling, it would be better if she didn't visit him in prison just yet. Shona gleaned from the little he had said that he was remaining in hospital for a few days, a compromise by the governor after he'd refused to go into segregation. The edge in his voice was enough to tell her that he hadn't changed his mind. Becca was under threat if he lodged an appeal. Shona, who had hoped to spare her daughter this news, now had no choice but to tell her. Delfont had targeted Becca in the past, when a criminal associate had tried to run her over, then finally held her hostage in a bid to make Shona back off from a related case. It had ended in the death of two men. Shona had no doubt the threat from Delfont was real.

Becca had listened calmly and had seemed to shrink into a silence that worried Shona more than any hysterical outburst. She looked genuinely shocked when Shona told her the rape case against Delfont had been dropped, and then her outrage on her mother's behalf burst forth in a torrent of angry tears and a vow to help Shona in any way she could to get the bastard. 'You can help me by staying safe,' Shona had said, and listed a series of precautions for Becca to follow. Stay at High Pines as much as possible. Don't open the door to strangers, ever. Always keep your phone on you. Be vigilant.

There had been an email in Shona's inbox from Anoushka, but it was late, and Shona hadn't read it, choosing to focus all her energy on reassuring her daughter. If Rob continued to stick to his guns, the barrister's work might all be in vain anyway.

Shona switched on the kettle and put a frozen croissant in the microwave. Then she dialled the bird warden.

Kyle Smith answered after the first ring. 'I was just about to call you.'

'You sound very bright for this time in the morning,' Shona replied, smiling. The six-foot-six, red-bearded giant had made a favourable impression at previous meetings. English-born of Scots-Irish parents, he'd arrived at the Mersehead reserve armed with an ecology degree, a sideline as a carpenter and boundless enthusiasm, even at the earliest of hours.

'I'm basically a giant lark,' he quipped. 'It's how I got the job.'

Shona relayed her guests' offer of help. When she mentioned the reserve, she heard him grunt in recognition.

'Send them down. They'll know all about HPAI.'

Highly pathogenic avian influenza. It seemed Kyle already had confirmation.

'The test results are back?' Shona said.

'It's why I was about to call you.' He sighed. 'H5N1 variant. No doubt about it.'

'Does that mean there'll be more bird deaths?'

'Yes. We've had the less lethal H7N3 strain around locally for a while. But H5N1 originated in poultry production in Asia, first spreading through stock movements but now largely by migrating birds. Flu impact compounds existing long-term human-caused pressures such as fishing, habitat loss and climate change. It's a particularly acute threat to long-lived seabirds like kittiwakes, guillemots and terns, which have slower breeding rates than geese.'

The notion there might be worse to come made Shona pause. The sight of all those dead birds in the firth was still firmly etched on her mind; she doubted she'd ever forget it.

'But no possibility poison was used on the Solway geese?'

'Very unlikely,' Kyle replied. 'We keep the grass in the saltmarshes at a level for the geese to graze. Some birds do spill over into the barley fields, where they're less welcome. I honestly don't think poison is a factor here, either from farmers or the protest group you were worried about. We've recorded over sixteen thousand avian flu deaths throughout Scotland this winter, just from the Svalbard population of barnacle geese that migrate here.'

'I'm sorry,' Shona said. 'It must be tough.'

'It's a war on all fronts,' Kyle said. 'The old folks here have a saying: *the arrival of the geese marks the departure of the swallows*. We're all holding our breath for the day that doesn't happen, when neither of those migrants make it home, when we go out on the marsh and there's silence. I used to think that was an exaggeration, but not now.'

Shona thanked him for the update and wished him well. As she chewed her croissant and swallowed paink-illers, she knew nature couldn't have a more committed champion than the man locals referred to as the Viking Birdwalker. She texted the guests a map to the reserve and Kyle's contact details, and got a thumbs up and heart emoji from them in return. A minute later she heard them drive off.

Shona called the film's director, Simon Jones, to update him on the birds' cause of death and emphasise they should still be vigilant over set security. His phone went straight to voicemail, probably down to the poor signal, so she left a message. Shona planned to go over to Hildan Island today with Tommy, who was picking up catering supplies and heading out on the early afternoon tide.

Becca came into the kitchen, yawning and stretching. She wasn't due on the set today. She looked at her mother's plate, then towards the unused oven, before she rolled her eyes.

'Who microwaves a croissant?' she said, appalled. 'It must be disgusting.'

It was, but Shona wasn't about to admit that.

Becca set the correct temperature without even looking at the dial, pulled out a baking tray and loaded it with three frozen croissants. 'Guests okay? I heard you talking to them.'

Shona relayed their desire to volunteer in the bird clean-up and the news from Kyle.

'Can I volunteer, too?' Becca said.

After the shock of the previous day, it was typical of her daughter to throw herself into fixing the problem, but Shona wasn't keen to re-expose Becca to the trauma of the environmental disaster, on top of the potential threat from Delfont.

'Think you need a bit of biohazard experience, darling.'

'I've suffered your cooking for the last three months.' Becca grinned. 'That makes me over-qualified.'

'Cheek.' Shona got up and flicked a dishtowel at her daughter. 'Anyways, if we're talking qualifications, you can catch up with your studies, since you had yesterday off.' It was a way of reminding her daughter of the need to stay at High Pines without bursting the fragile bubble of the normality both were striving hard to maintain.

'Ah, but I didn't really have a day off,' Becca replied. 'I was talking to Barry the script guy and he gave me loads of good stuff.' She slid the baking tray into the oven and sat down at the table. 'Did you know Burns owned banned books, including Thomas Paine's *Rights of Man*? That comes up a lot on my literature course. It's really political philosophy, and Barry said it's mostly about the tax system.' Becca made a face. 'But that I should pay careful attention to its key issues if I want to understand Burns's motivation. I'll get mega points if I quote it in my essay.'

Shona was impressed. 'That shows initiative. Well done.'

'Oh, and I'm going to be a maid…' Becca continued, then paused before asking, 'I can still go on set, right?'

Shona calculated that the island location, the film's dedicated security team and her own presence made the set the best option after High Pines.

'Good,' Becca said firmly, and Shona was cheered a little by her daughter's buoyant defiance in not letting the threat send her into hiding.

'The scene,' Becca continued, 'is where Burns is hauled in front of his bosses for refusing to take his hat off or stand up for "God Save the King" at a theatre and for almost getting in a duel because some geezer thought he'd toasted the French Revolution.' She took the tray from the oven and deposited a perfectly baked croissant on her mother's plate. 'And he might get hanged for it,' Becca finished with relish.

Shona was about to point out that Burns died in his own bed, and she'd witnessed it herself, when her phone rang: Simon Jones returning her call.

'DI Oliver, can you help us out?' he said. 'Michael Vincent has... er... gone off.'

She was going to make a joke about actors and their use-by dates, when she caught the edge in Simon's voice. 'What d'you mean, gone off?'

'He took a boat last night and went in search of... supplies. He hasn't come back.'

'You mean drugs?'

'Drugs, booze, whatever. He can handle a boat. Grew up in Windermere. But he's not come back.' Simon paused. 'Thing is, last time he ended up in custody. Gave a false name. His lawyer smoothed things. Kept it quiet.'

'And you want me to check he's not banged up in Dumfries police office?'

'If you could.'

Shona exhaled loudly. 'Give me an hour.'

Chapter 13

Shona gave Becca strict instructions to stay at home, not open the door and get on with her studies. She'd be back from Dumfries in time for them both to catch the boat with Tommy.

Shona had just left the A75, heading for the town centre, when her phone rang. Amanda Collins, chair of the B&B owners' group. Shona gave an involuntary shudder. She loathed the woman, and sensed the feeling was mutual, but she needed the group's support. Amanda adored Rob and regarded Shona as a floundering amateur, which was harsh but fair. Shona clicked the hands-free.

'Hi, Amanda.' Shona could picture her, all smooth hair and statement jewellery.

'Shona. I won't keep you. Quick favour. We'd like James McGowan to be our Burns at the Burns Supper. Address the haggis, and all that.'

If you'd met him, you really wouldn't, thought Shona. 'Have you contacted his agent?'

'I can't wait any longer for a reply.' Amanda huffed. 'Ask him. It's for charity. You have the in.'

'I doubt me asking would make any difference. The film schedule is pretty tight, and he's a vegetarian.' Shona pulled out to avoid a cyclist.

There was the briefest pause and Shona thought the line had dropped, but Amanda's clipped tone came back loud and clear.

'Look, Shona, we want to continue to support you, even though the group is really just for B&Bs. You're more of a holiday let now,' she said, with distaste. The implication was clear. In Rob's absence Shona was allowing High Pines to deteriorate perilously close to the thing the owners most despised: an Airbnb.

Shona gritted her teeth. 'Fine. I'll try. But I have to warn you, he's very method,' she said, borrowing Simon Jones's phrase.

'I don't know what that is, but I'm sure it can be made to work. Thanks, Shona. Must dash.'

It would almost be worth setting a full-throttle McGowan loose on Amanda's carefully organised Burns Supper, just to see her expression, but that wasn't going to happen. Maybe she could get a signed something-or-other they could raffle, and Shona would be off the hook.

She fought the rest of her way through the snarl of early traffic. When she arrived at Loreburn, she sent off a polite text to the number listed for James McGowan in her contacts and hoped one of his assistants would sort it out.

The custody suite at Loreburn police office in Dumfries was a two-minute drive from her CID office at Cornwall Mount, and the most likely destination of anyone picked up by the response teams the night before. Scotland's twelve-hour initial custody rule meant that offenders normally went before the sheriff the next morning and she couldn't see how someone as famous as Michael Vincent could conceal his identity. Simon had assured her that his acting skills had carried him through before, right up until his lawyer arrived with profuse apologies on the actor's behalf and convincing stories of undercover research for *Baker Street* that Vincent had, mistakenly, taken a little too far.

The custody sergeant, Gerry McGuiness, took in Shona's RNLI jacket, jeans and just fading black eye from behind his Perspex screen. He was stocky, all shoulders and neck, wearing a Police Scotland half-zipped microfleece.

'Cannae keep away, can you?' he said. 'I hear banana bread's the thing.'

Shona frowned. 'Thing for what, Gerry?'

'Being bored at home. Did you no' bring me a slice?'

'I'm not on leave. It's a liaison job.'

'Oh aye, gadding aboot wi' film stars, I heard.' Gerry shook his head. 'If it was Scarlett Johansson, you could put me down fur an autograph. Lilly Chase is a pocket rocket, sure enough, but I'm no' into her music. Prefer country and western, me.'

'I'll be sure to tell her,' Shona replied.

'I might consider a crossover album, if she ditched the funny claes. Shoes that make ye look like a lobster do nuthin' fur a lassie.'

'Gerry,' Shona said, with thinning patience. Gerry McGuiness was a solid cop. She had a lot of time for him, just not this morning. 'I need to ask you about your overnight customers.'

'Aye, sorry. What can I do ye for?'

'Male. Early forties. Slim build.' Shona wondered about the long, blonde curls. Might be a wig. She left out the hair colour. 'A new face, not one of your frequent fliers. Likely alcohol related or possibly possession of a Class A?'

The sergeant ran one hand over his cropped scalp as he scrolled down the screen with the other. He stuck out his bottom lip and shook his head.

'Just my regulars, and a lassie the Specials brought in. She's had a bit of bad luck. I'm trying to get her a psych evaluation.'

Shona knew that meant the girl had probably been talked down from a high building or tried to throw herself in front of a train. Gerry was blunt and brash, but he tried to prevent repeat business if he could.

'Do you want me tae bell you if the fella comes in?'

Shona thought for a minute. If Vincent wasn't in custody by now, he might well be making his own way back to Hildan Island. Or he could have passed out, stoned, in some girl's flat only to be attacked by an irate pimp or boyfriend.

'Thanks, pal,' Shona said. 'That'd be great.'

'Anyways, good luck wi' yer flash movie gig.' He picked up his Queen o' the South football mug and slipped off his stool, heading for a refill.

'It's not nearly as glamorous as you think, Gerry.'

'I'm thinking it's more glamourous than moppin' oot vomit fae a cell.'

The custody sergeant buzzed open the door to the carpark for her.

'Okay, Gerry. I'll give you that one.' Shona smiled, as she pulled the handle and went back out into the drizzly morning.

She rang Simon Jones with the news. Michael Vincent hadn't returned. The film crew had searched the island, but without any luck.

After she hung up, she called the coastguard to report Vincent as a missing person. It might garner him more bad press, but he'd had his chance. No one had seen him for twelve hours and the Solway Firth wasn't Windermere. Irritated as she was by his behaviour, she was now concerned for his safety.

She drove to Cornwall Mount CID office, parked behind the building and took the stairs to the top floor, reflecting they felt a little easier than the last time.

A few of the civilian staff clocked her entrance, eyes swivelling towards her office and then jumping nervously back, like carriages on an old-fashioned type-writer. Murdo, Kate and Ravi were absent from their desks. Shona went straight to her office door, gave a light knock and entered without waiting for a reply.

DI Kenneth Dalrymple looked up from where he was pacing the carpet, his thumbs hooked in the waistcoat of his tweed suit. He had a square face with a strong jawline and thinning hair, and projected an unthreatening authority, like a country doctor or a vet in a TV drama set in the 1950s. He was only lacking a pipe to complete the picture. Given his beat in a largely rural area with an ageing population, Shona wondered if he cultivated the image on purpose.

'Ah, Shona. Come in,' he said, as if she'd arrived for a consultation about infertility in her border terrier. He extended his hand then indicated for her to take a seat in front of her desk, while he sat in her usual chair.

'Your arsonist, Joe Dylan,' he began in his soft, educated Scots accent. 'He has an alibi for the night of the fatal house fire. Did you know?' Shona shook her head and he continued, 'He was at a friend's flat in Manchester. CCTV places him in venues at the time of the fire.'

Shona couldn't work out if Dalrymple was keeping her in the loop, or trying to find out if someone else was doing just that.

'Have the SFRS investigators pinned down the cause of the fire yet?' she asked.

'Murdo's over there at the minute,' he replied. 'And to what do we owe the pleasure of your visit this morning?'

His question was full of politeness, but Shona would have taken it better if the man hadn't been sitting in her chair, in her office.

'Kate's pulling up some background for me on the actors.'

'Ah yes, commandeering our Kate for a bit of celebrity chasing.' He smiled indulgently.

'We'll be doing a bit more "celebrity chasing" if Michael Vincent doesn't turn up soon,' Shona said, icily. Kenny Dalrymple was, by all accounts, a capable officer, but his laid-back manner was beginning to grate on her.

'Is he at risk, d'you think?'

She couldn't really claim that he was. Now they knew avian flu was behind the dead birds, there was no threat from the Arctic Guardians, or anyone else beyond over-enthusiastic fans.

'He appears to have gone on a bender,' Shona replied. 'But he took a boat, and that's always a worry. Not answering his phone. Coastguard are aware.'

'Ah, here's Murdo now,' Dalrymple said, for all the world as if they'd been waiting on a final dinner guest.

Murdo opened the door to the office. His face was red, as though he'd hurried up the stairs. One side of his shirt had worked loose from his grey suit trousers, and he was hauling them up and re-tucking at the same time. He looked from Shona to Dalrymple, and back again, as if he'd entered a topsy-turvy world of multiple bosses.

'The fire was caused by an iPad,' Murdo said. 'Seems the wee lassie, Taylor, got it for Christmas and had put it inside her school bag, maybe to show her friends.' He delivered the news like a referee at a tennis match, constantly switching his gaze from one DI to the other. 'It was still plugged into the charger and overheated. There's a socket just by the front door.'

Dalrymple said nothing but nodded slowly.

Shona struggled to hold her tongue, until eventually the DI spoke.

'I see,' he said. 'So, the cause of the fire was accidental?'

'Well, there's a bit more to it than that,' Murdo said. 'A charging tablet wouldn't normally generate that amount of heat. The fire service tech guys traced the iPad to a batch of fakes on the Trading Standards watchlist. They've been working with Customs, checking lorries coming in at Dover and Hull, but also Cairnryan.'

Shona felt her anger rising. 'You're saying there's a criminal gang operating in Dumfries and Galloway who're responsible for the death of two people, one of them an eight-year-old girl?'

'That's about the size of it,' Murdo replied.

Dalrymple's jawline hardened and Shona finally glimpsed steel beneath the affable exterior. 'Does Mrs Nicolson know where the iPad came from?'

'Got Ravi to ask her. She said the husband, Sean, bought it. No chance of finding a receipt wi' the state of the house. We're checking their bank accounts, but it's likely he used cash.'

'Okay. I've a contact at the National Crime Agency,' Dalrymple said, and leaned forward, picking up his phone.

'Murdo, get onto the Customs team and the port control room at Cairnryan, tell them I sent you. I want all they have. We need to target every retailer, market stall and one-man-band. Trading Standards have probably called, but a cop in uniform talking about the culpable homicide of a child might shake a supplier's name loose.' He turned to Shona. 'I'm sorry, you'll have to excuse us.' He nodded through the glass to where Kate and Ravi stood, trying not to be caught grandstanding. 'I can give you DC Irving for half an hour, but I'm going to need her back.' He began making notes with a fountain pen on a pad in front of him.

'Five minutes will do.' Shona got up. 'You should add pubs and working men's clubs to the list. Pre-Christmas would've been busy, but it's possible they'd remember someone offering cheap iPads to customers. And you might get lucky with CCTV.'

'Useful idea,' Dalrymple said, pointing his pen at her in a way that Shona found deeply patronising. She fought the unpleasant sensation she been catapulted back to her time as a DC again. There was a mental list of actions she'd want implemented, but this was Dalrymple's case now. She said her goodbyes, conscious of Murdo's nervous gaze on her as she did so.

Kate said she'd email the background information on the actors, so Shona took a free desk next to the civilian team of data analyst Chloe Burke and Vincent Grieg, their visual investigations officer, known to all as Vinny Visuals. Chloe gave her a welcoming smile, while Vinny merely blinked at this unprecedented glitch in the matrix.

While Shona waited for Kate's file, she scrolled through her inbox, stopping at the previous night's email from Anoushka. She had to reply to it eventually. The barrister was aware of Rob's decision to drop the appeal idea. As an old school friend of his, Anoushka had put in a lot of work pro bono and Shona didn't want her to think that she, at least, wasn't grateful for the barrister's efforts. Shona clicked on the message.

A woman called Katherine Jones from Australia claimed she had evidence that would clear Rob. Shona frowned. The name meant nothing. Ms Jones had been living at her family's sheep farm in Australia and hadn't been following UK news. Later, when she heard about the trial, she'd assumed that what she knew wasn't important and Rob would get off. It sounded far-fetched to Shona. City of London Police must have tracked down every possible witness in a complex investigation with many millions at stake. It wasn't unknown for oddballs to come out of the woodwork, only to later admit the identity of the perpetrator had come to them in a dream or been revealed by their spirit guide.

Googling such a common name as Katherine Jones predictably brought up dozens of hits, none of which meant anything to Shona. Anoushka, however, was convinced it was worth pursuing. Shona glanced at her watch. It had been a couple of hours since she'd spoken to Becca and she had the sudden urge to check on her daughter.

'Do you remember a friend of your dad's called Katherine Jones?' Shona said on impulse when Becca answered.

'Nope, but I was a kid in London. If she had a puppy or wore funny hats, I might know her. Why? Is it important? Does she know something that will help Dad?'

Sharp as a tack, my daughter. Should've remembered that, Shona thought, hearing the hope in Becca's voice.

'Maybe. Apparently, she's been living on a sheep farm in Australia,' she said, the scepticism in her voice audible even to her.

Becca had no such doubts. 'It's Kanga. Dad's Australian PA, I think. She used to come to the house sometimes, to drop him off. She gave me the little kangaroo for my birthday, remember?'

Shona racked her brains, but there was nothing. 'Okay, darling. Thanks. Everything okay?'

'Fine, Mum. I'll see you at lunch. I'm doing soup. Carrot and coriander.'

'Great. Be there in an hour.'

Shona sent off a quick thank you to Anoushka, saying she'd talk to Rob about Katherine Jones, before pulling up Kate's comprehensive background reports on James McGowan and Michael Vincent. She'd clocked the allegation of sexual assault against Vincent by an American actress, when her phone rang.

'Belfast Coastguard just tasked the lifeboat tae recover a fatality fae Hildan Island,' Tommy said.

Shona felt her stomach drop. 'Is it Vincent?'

'Lookin' that way. Graham Finlayson on helm, wi' a couple of the new boys. *Silver Crest* is here if you need her.'

Shona stood up and looked back at her office. Dalrymple was the on-call DI and he was also on his feet, phone clamped to his ear. His expression indicated he'd heard the news. Technically, it was his case, but he pointed a finger at her, then at the door. *It's yours*, he mouthed. *Go.*

Chapter 14

As Shona went down the stairs, she called the uniform inspector and asked for a Kirsty. Either would do – PC Kirsten O'Carroll or PC Christine Jamieson, collectively known as the Two Kirsties, from the translation of their first names into the all-encompassing Scots colloquial form. There was a special offer on, the inspector told her. She could BOGOF: buy one, get one free. Probably not the first time he'd made that joke, but she'd gladly have both. He rarely split the pair anyway, he said: a criminal apocalypse might ensue. Jokes aside, separately they were experienced, efficient officers. Together, O'Carroll's formidable natural authority and Jamieson's approachability made them the response cop's dream team.

A half hour later, Shona arrived at Kirkness. To her surprise she saw Tommy rowing back from the *Ramsey Ranger*, dour-faced and with his big blue toolbox in the bottom of the boat. Shona's money was on Freya, whose rural Orkney upbringing inclined her to offer help wherever it was needed, arm-twisting Tommy into taking on at least some of the repairs. Becca was standing on the quayside, large Thermos in hand.

'Soup,' she said, handing the flask to her mother. 'Some's for Tommy.' She eyed the squad fourbie that had pulled up behind Shona's Audi, and the uniform officers, in the shape of the Two Kirsties, that stepped out. 'Is it true Michael Vincent's dead?'

'Who told you that?' Shona said, anxiously. The film set was probably a sieve, but she didn't want news leaking out before ID was confirmed and any family informed.

'Heard you on the phone this morning, about him being missing,' Becca replied. 'Saw the lifeboat go out. Plus, this.' She wagged a finger up and down at the two officers. 'I'm not daft. What happened?'

'We don't know it's him for sure.'

Shona was torn between taking Becca with her to Hildan, where she could keep a close eye on her, and leaving her alone at High Pines, thereby protecting her from what was sure to be a grim and deeply unpleasant business. She plumped for the latter.

'Listen, I know I said you could come, but I think it's better if you stay here.'

She thought Becca might argue but her daughter simply nodded.

'Call Freya, or Callum, if you're worried or need anything,' Shona said. Callum – a postman – started early and was often around the village in the afternoons. 'I'll be back soon as I can.'

'Will the filming be cancelled?'

'For today. Maybe tomorrow. Beyond that, I really don't know.'

Tommy had the engine running on the *Silver Crest*. The two officers were loading portable arc lights and other kit from their car. A CSI was on their way from Glasgow, but they'd need to preserve any potential crime scene, including the *Margaret Wilson* if the lifeboat recovered the casualty. Ideally, the body would have remained in situ until forensics arrived, but the tide and the shortness of the January day put paid to that idea.

'Go home, darlin',' Shona said, and hugged her. 'Go on. I'll watch you. Wave to me from the big window.'

Shona watched as Becca grinned and set off at a run. By the time the boat left her mooring, Becca would be home safe. The Two Kirsties stood on the aft deck of the *Silver Crest*, thumbs hooked in the armholes of their fluorescent utility vests, ready for whatever Shona, or the sea, could throw at them.

Shona undid the bow rope and stepped aboard. With little wind in the sheltered anchorage, the drizzle hung in curtains across the estuary, stippling the gunmetal surface of the flat water. The hour-long crossing should be smoother this time, and retrieving the body less hazardous for the RNLI crew. The recovery operation for the dead birds had moved further east overnight, so at least they should be spared that. As the old fishing boat swung out into mid-channel, Shona turned and looked back at High Pines. There was Becca in the window of the top-floor lounge, waving as she often did when her mother was out on a shout with the lifeboat. Shona waved back, reassured Becca was safe, then went below for soup and strategy-planning with the Two Kirsties.

–

From the moment Shona arrived at the scene she had no doubt that it was Michael Vincent's body that lay at the foot of the high cliffs near the Captain's Eye. At the top, a knot of crew and extras huddled together twenty metres back from the edge, as if physical proximity to each other would ward off whatever had struck the actor down.

Shona barked at the three black-clad men from set security to get everyone back to Hildan House and keep them there.

Vincent was face down, body strangely twisted, his blonde curls darkened by blood almost to the colour of the black rocks around him. In his long brown coat and dark jeans, it wasn't surprising he hadn't been spotted earlier. From what Shona could see from this high up, his clothes were wet. But it had been raining almost constantly since the early hours, never mind the spray from the sea. He was above the high-water line so it was more likely he had fallen, rather than been washed ashore.

Shona ordered the clifftop taped off, although the ground was already churned by the film crew's footprints, and then she sent the Two Kirsties back to Hildan House to begin collecting statements. After unloading the food supplies, Tommy had taken the *Silver Crest* back to Kirkness to wait for the scenes of crime officer. The *Margaret Wilson* floated offshore, riding the low swell: Shona guessed Tommy's willingness to act as a glorified water taxi was partly so he could make sure the RNLI station was ready to receive Vincent's body with the due care and respect they extended to every casualty.

She took the final shots with her phone, then raised Graham Finlayson on the VHF radio handset that Tommy had given her.

'Kirkness lifeboat, Kirkness lifeboat, be advised you can now proceed with recovery. Please be forensically aware. Standing by.'

'Received.' Finlayson raised a hand to her on the clifftop, then brought the D-class lifeboat as close as he could to the rock slabs at the base of the cliff. The other two crew in their drysuits and white helmets scrambled ashore, carrying a folded orange body bag and a yellow tote containing a flexible plastic stretcher. They weren't trained in evidence recovery, but Shona trusted them to retrieve not only the body, but also any clothing, shoes or personal items that were close by. She watched until they were safely back in the *Margaret Wilson*, Vincent cocooned in his plastic shroud and on his way to the mortuary ambulance waiting outside Kirkness lifeboat station.

'Graham, did you find anything with the casualty? Personal effects? Or a weapon?' Shona said over the radio.

There was the hiss and crackle of an open channel, then Graham Finlayson's reply: 'Negative, Shona.'

'Thank you, Kirkness lifeboat,' Shona replied. 'Safe home.'

From above, the impressive sea arch of the Captain's Eye was invisible, reduced to a narrow ledge that ran out like a grassy gangplank, fifty metres above the hungry sea. There was no path down to the shoreline. Access for the crime scene technician would be a long and tricky scramble across the rocks from the beach where they'd filmed earlier and might ultimately be a fruitless exercise.

Michael Vincent's death was either an accident, suicide or caused by the involvement of a third party, resulting in a culpable homicide or murder. Simon Jones thought he'd gone off in a boat. She'd reported the missing three-metre Zodiac RIB but it hadn't been found drifting or wrecked. If he had gone over the cliff edge, what had he been doing up here in the dark on a freezing January night? And was he alone?

By the time the crime scene technician had arrived at the scene, it was growing dark, although lights had been set up at the taped-off area of the clifftop. Billy Campbell – a newbie SOCO with a by-the-book attitude

– threw up his hands when faced with the churned-up patch of muddy grass and the impossibility of accessing the foot of the cliff. Shona informed him that he needed to adjust his expectations when it came to the chaos of crime scenes, or he would be in for a lifetime of disappointments. After morosely recording what he could, Billy Campbell searched Vincent's room with the aid of PC Christine Jamieson, bagging a phone and a wallet.

A westerly wind had sprung up, driving off the rain. In different circumstances this would be balm for the soul. Shona had climbed to the brow of the hill above the leafless woodland surrounding the house, the close-crowded topmost twigs wisps of greys and browns like frozen smoke against the fire of the winter sunset. She took a deep breath, pulling in the fresh, salty scent of the sea. Far out in the firth, white waves frilled across the sandbars like ghosts of the vanished geese. Closer in, channel buoys blinked red and green against the grey as toothed sawblades of rock pushed up between the frothing water. Last night, under a bright moon and racing storm clouds, the view must have been spectacular, but she didn't think that was what had drawn Michael Vincent to the clifftop. She had one chance to get this right before the family and the press began demanding answers.

Glancing at her phone, Shona saw two signal bars. She should call in to Dalrymple, keep him in the loop even if he appeared to have handed the case to her.

Once she'd updated him, she said, 'You're happy for me to continue on this?'

He was more senior to her in years served, although probably not in the variety of their experience. Who wouldn't want to be SIO in such a high-profile death?

'You're on the spot. We'd lose time getting me up to speed, and everyone knows the first twenty-four hours are crucial. I've squared it with Davies.'

Dalrymple, it seemed, wasn't driven by personal ambition. She'd heard his hobby was fly-fishing and he had a wife who'd been described to her as *mentally fragile*. Reason enough to stay in Galloway, with its quieter pace of life. Perhaps they weren't so different after all. She'd returned to Rob's home village three years ago, when things got rough for them all in London. Her daughter's expulsion for drug possession and Rob leaving Milton McConnell had brought them here, but when she'd been offered a promotion that meant a move to Glasgow, she hadn't taken it. If it wasn't for Rob's incarceration, Delfont, and the threats to Becca, she'd also be in danger of becoming that rarest of things – a police officer happy with her lot. It was a truth she was sometimes uncomfortably aware of.

She walked back down the track to Hildan House. Small groups of now familiar faces, crew and extras, stood talking quietly and smoking by the main entrance. The Two Kirsties would've warned them not to stray. As she approached, the heavily muscled security guard she'd seen on the set in Dumfries pulled himself to attention in a way that told her he was probably ex-military.

'Matt?' she said, dredging up his name from her memory.

'Yes, ma'am?' he said.

'Who found the body?'

'Lighting rigger, Terry Dowland. Shook him up.' He nodded to a lean, forty-something man in a Boat Hoose hoodie, chain-smoking in a manner that was sure to knock a few years off his life expectancy. 'Head for heights. Said he'd search the cliffs. Terry has ropework experience. He called me. Talked about going down to Vincent, but soon as I looked, I knew he was a goner. Best leave it to you.'

'Thank you. You did the right thing. Everyone else is accounted for from the cast and crew?'

He nodded. That put paid to her theory of a guilty party fleeing the island in the Zodiac after an altercation, but it didn't mean a culprit wasn't still in their midst.

'The other day,' she continued, 'you said there'd been a few problems with fans generally. Any previous issues with Michael Vincent?'

There was a flicker in his otherwise impassive dark eyes. 'How d'you mean?'

'Specific fans. Arguments with anyone on the set? Erratic behaviour on Mr Vincent's part?'

'Not that I can recall.'

Shona pursed her lips. 'Well, if you do think of anything, be sure to let me, or one of my officers, know.' She nodded past him to where the Two Kirsties were cross-checking a list of cast and crew names against their notebooks. 'I'm sure your company's reputation is important to you, and you'd like this cleared up quickly.'

'Yes, ma'am.' He stood expressionless once more, eyes ahead.

She walked through the open doors into the wood-panelled main hall, slowing to let her eyes adjust to the dimness. The shaded wall lights, which had been dismantled and removed for yesterday's scene, had been returned to their positions but were doing little to dispel the gloom.

Simon Jones came forward to greet her. He looked pale and hadn't shaved, and the circles under his eyes told their own story of a sleepless night.

'I've given the contact details of Michael's family to your officer,' the director said.

'Simon, the missing boat? Who does it belong to?'

'The security company, but I don't know if they own it or hired it.'

'And what made you think Michael Vincent took it?'

Simon looked a little sheepish. 'I stopped him heading off the night before. Security came down to the pier. We made light of it. He said he just wanted to take it for a spin around the island, let off some steam, but we all agreed it wasn't safe in the dark.'

From out of the shadows, and without so much as a greeting, McGowan launched straight in. 'What happened to Mikey?'

He looked distraught. The cynical question of whether he was more upset at his friend's death, or the potential torpedoing of his film, was foremost in Shona's mind, although she tried not to let it show. He was probably in shock, and so deserved the same treatment as any other witness, despite her contempt for his previous behaviour.

'It looks as if he may have fallen,' she replied. 'Who saw him last?'

'Me, I think,' McGowan said. 'We did a bit of a Burns reading for everyone. A two-hander, some ballads. Then he went up tae bed just after ten o'clock.'

'And no one heard him go out?'

Both men shook their heads.

'Any reason why he might have gone back to the cliffs beside the Captain's Eye?' Shona watched McGowan chewing his lip as he shook his head again.

'None,' McGowan said emphatically. 'But I do know one thing. Whatever happened... when he got there, he was wearing my coat.'

Chapter 15

Just before eight a.m. the next morning, Shona pressed the buzzer at Dumfries and Galloway Royal Infirmary mortuary. Slasher Sue appeared, already in her green scrubs. Professor Sue Kitchen was as quick with a scalpel as she had been with an épée, the heaviest of sporting swords, during her long reign as Scottish National Fencing Champion. Beneath her surgical cap, the cropped curls had faded to grey. At six-foot tall, and with a muscular physique retained by training with the rowing club, she towered over Shona's diminutive form.

They'd come from very different beginnings, but both had risen in male-dominated professions and, on past cases, they'd discovered they shared a laser-like determination for uncovering the truth. *We speak for the dead* was Professor Kitchen's oft-repeated motto, and Shona couldn't agree more.

'I'm so glad it's you,' Shona said to her friend. 'Thanks for coming down so early on a Saturday.'

'That was heartfelt,' Professor Kitchen replied, clapping her on the shoulder. 'This case giving you more trouble than usual?' She tilted her head towards the post-mortem suite where Michael Vincent's body was being prepped, probably by Professor Kitchen's regular senior pathology technician, Ciara Newburgh.

'The Super is doin' his nut. The press and higher-ups have melted his phone, wanting to know the hows and whys of Vincent's death. Social media is hoachin' with theories, everything from an FBI hit to aliens.'

'Well, we'll do our best to get you some answers,' the pathology professor replied. 'Might be sticking my neck out here, but even at this stage, we can probably rule out aliens.'

As Shona changed into a scrub suit, she reflected that if anyone could find answers it was Professor Kitchen. Her department at Glasgow University held the contract for performing post-mortems with Scotland's Crown Office and, in addition to research and teaching, the seven consultant pathologists performed more than two thousand autopsies every year in the west of Scotland, ranging from fatal accidents and drug-related deaths to homicides.

When Shona re-joined the professor, Ciara was already moving with intent around the PM table.

Although Shona had seen Michael Vincent's body in situ at the foot of the cliff, the damage to his face was far greater than she'd expected. It was hardly a face at all. Even ID confirmation with dental records would have been tricky. Only his general stature, and the mop of long blonde curls, remained of the actor previously instantly recognisable by millions of TV fans.

'You've just missed your Ravi,' Ciara said. 'He was here with Mr Vincent's father. We suggested DNA would be a better option to confirm ID, and he agreed.'

'Thank you,' Shona said. It would have been a difficult encounter for family member and staff, and she trusted both Ravi and Ciara to have handled it sensitively.

Michael Vincent's clothing was carefully removed and bagged for transfer to the Scottish Police Authority

Forensic Services at Gartcosh. Shona eyed the coat. She had no doubt it was the one she'd seen McGowan wearing as Robert Burns.

Professor Kitchen did a whirlwind tour of the table, recorded her initial impressions, then stood back as Ciara made the Y-shaped incision, opening Vincent's torso. Organs were decanted with speed and efficiency to be examined and weighed, and samples taken. A second cut was made at the back of the skull. Twenty minutes later, the pathologist turned to Shona.

'Everything I'm seeing is consistent with a fall from height onto a hard surface. The cause of death is catastrophic injuries to head and chest.'

'We were initially told he'd taken a boat off the island,' Shona said. 'Any chance he went overboard and was deposited on the shore?'

'No water in the lungs.' Professor Kitchen lifted Vincent's hand and examined the fingertips. 'And there's no evidence of skin saturation. I'd expect wider soft tissue damage if he'd been washed across rocks.'

Shona nodded. It confirmed what she'd believed when she first saw Vincent. At least she could discount the missing boat as a crime scene.

'Even before we get the toxicology results,' Professor Kitchen continued, 'I think we can say he was a one-man walking pharmaceutical cornucopia. See this?' The pathologist pulled aside a flap of skin that had once covered Vincent's nose, revealing a series of round perforations. 'Septum damage that's not linked to the fall.' She turned his lower arm outwards. 'Old track marks. The smell of alcohol was also present in the stomach contents.' She turned her piercing gaze to Shona. 'We have an individual showing signs of poly-addiction, wandering about in the dark, and falling from a cliff. Does that tally with your working hypothesis?'

'A fall does seem the most likely scenario,' Shona agreed. 'But is there any evidence he could have been pushed?'

'You're thinking defensive injuries, yes?'

When Shona nodded, Professor Kitchen said, 'We've taken parings in case there's any foreign DNA under his nails, but I'm not hopeful. There are abrasions to hands, arms, face, but this is where it gets a little tricky. The wounds were sufficiently ante-mortem for bruising to form, probably by several hours. But they are consistent with a fight.'

'Or a kidnap,' Shona said.

Sue looked at her enquiringly. 'Fascinating. Do tell.'

Shona recounted the scene she'd watched the morning before Michael Vincent's death. His encounter with the smuggling gang out to capture him and the immersive nature of the filming.

'Aren't they supposed to have stunt people for that sort of thing?' the professor asked.

'Oh, they have a fight co-ordinator. Who's also the armourer: looks after the pistols and swords.'

'What sort of swords?' Professor Kitchen said, her interest immediately aroused.

'Dunno,' Shona replied. 'Big ones. Becca was in among it all. It was full-on. Folk getting banjoed left, right and centre. My heart was in my mouth at times, but she took it all in her stride. Loved it.'

'Good girl. I'd expect no less.' The professor grinned. She'd long had her eye on Becca as a potential university fencing team recruit and had actively encouraged her to apply to Glasgow's prestigious archaeology course.

'I didn't see any injuries on Michael Vincent, but he was in the thick of it.'

'That makes it difficult to rule out a further violent encounter later the same day,' Sue said, and nodded to her assistant, a sign she could proceed with replacing organs and closing the body.

'Listen, you look like you could do with a coffee,' the professor said, eyeing Shona. 'And I could certainly do with one. Let's get out of Ciara's way while she finishes up.'

Ten minutes later, they were changed into their street clothes and sitting at a table by the window in the hospital's almost empty cafe, two machine coffees in front of them.

'How are you holding up?' Professor Kitchen said, spearing Shona with her piercing gaze.

Shona knew Sue was referring to Rob's absence. She was desperate to avoid a forensic examination of her predicament by a mind as sharp as Sue's, even if it was motivated by genuine concern for a friend. 'He's not having an easy time of it in prison.'

Sue's expression betrayed her belief that it was nothing more than he deserved.

'But we're fine,' Shona said. 'I'm fine.'

'You should go home. Recharge. Sleep,' the professor said. 'I've clients in my freezer with more colour in their cheeks than you have.'

'Thanks for that. Your bedside manner hasn't grown rusty after all these years in the pathology lab.'

'I generally get no complaints.' Sue smiled. 'Tell me how Michael Vincent appeared when you last saw him.'

Perhaps her friend had picked up on Shona's reluctance to talk about Rob, or had learned as much as she wanted to know. Either way, it was a change of subject that Shona was profoundly grateful for.

She thought back to the beach below the Captain's Eye, and Michael Vincent becoming aware of her gaze and turning to smile at her. The established presence of alcohol on a dry set, and the possibility of drugs, meant she'd need to re-interview the cast and crew.

'He and Burns were on a boys' adventure to catch smugglers. They were both wired with adrenaline, but nothing struck me as odd.'

'You're talking about them as their characters in the movie,' Sue said with amusement. 'What's your sense of both actors as individuals?'

Vincent she'd hardly known, but he'd struck her as vain, shallow and self-destructive. Perhaps, on longer acquaintance, she'd have understood what led him down that path. James McGowan had proved to be a total disappointment. Perhaps in her hormone-driven schoolgirl naivety she'd projected qualities onto him that he'd never possessed. Sue was watching her again with that scalpel-tipped gaze so Shona played for time.

'Why do you ask?'

Sue shrugged. 'Just curious. High functioning indicates high tolerance, and the condition of his organs backs up that theory. What was his mental health like? I can screen the bloods for prescription meds.'

'In his statement, the director, Simon Jones, said Vincent had previously suffered from depression. The film's insurers insisted on a full medical prior to filming, which didn't mention any current health issues or prescription medication. Given his rumoured history, they'd have gone over it with a fine-tooth comb.'

'What about suicide? Any note?'

'Not that we've found.' Shona sipped her coffee. 'He wasn't carrying his phone or wallet. Would you say that indicated intent? So that he couldn't be contacted?'

'Maybe. Medically, I can't rule out suicide, but if ever the term *hellbent on self-destruction* applied to anyone, it was Michael Vincent. He was forty-two, but had the heart of a much older man. It's possible the drug use caused a sudden drop in blood pressure, and he blacked out and fell. So natural causes are also a possibility.'

'Then the cause of death is catastrophic head and chest injuries, but the medical evidence doesn't point strongly to either suicide, accidental death or murder?'

'All are possible,' the professor agreed.

Shona let out a long sigh. She'd hoped for a more conclusive outcome, knowing all the while it would be unlikely without CCTV, witnesses, a weapon or firm evidence of another's involvement. She thought back to Kate's briefing notes.

'Potentially, anyone who has a serious narcotics habit is likely to owe money to some very bad people. Then there's the actress who claims he assaulted her during an audition. We'll look at them, but I can't see either of those lines of enquiry leading anywhere.' Shona shook her head. 'And why kill him now? Much easier to wait until he got back to his London flat.'

Sue leaned back and folded her arms. 'There's something else, isn't there? Why do you think it's murder?'

'The clothes,' Shona said, remembering the evidence bags sitting ready for transfer to the forensic service at Gartcosh. She pinched the bridge of her nose between finger and thumb, then rubbed her eyes. 'The coat doesn't belong to him. It's one of two identical garments used as part of Burns's costume, worn by James McGowan. It's a freezing January night. You go out in a borrowed coat, onto a dangerous clifftop. Why?'

'Is it possible he was meeting someone?'

'You mean like a lassie? Or a dealer?' Shona considered. 'I wondered that. The company is limited. There's only thirty-two people on the island. Most are in shared accommodation and have accounted for each other, but he had his own room. If he wanted a private hook-up, and it would be entirely within character, why not go there? And there's another thing that's bugging me.'

'Forensics didn't find any drug paraphernalia in his room?' the professor said.

'Exactly.' Shona struck an emphatic point on the tabletop with her forefinger. 'Although he could've hidden it somewhere else – the place probably has secret passages and priest holes as standard. Security said they had no issues with Vincent's behaviour, yet the night before he'd tried to go off on a joyride with their Zodiac RIB, worth around twenty grand. If they weren't keeping a close eye on him, they should have been.'

'Going back to the coat, you're wondering if this James McGowan was the target?'

'He's wondering the same,' Shona replied, then told Sue what had happened when the dead geese were found. 'An armed fan got into his home recently. It's possible he's displaying an element of hyper-vigilance relating to that experience.'

'Could they be mistaken for each other? I'm not familiar with either actor.'

'Normally, I'd say no. Vincent is taller, less stocky, and those blonde curls are quite distinctive.'

'But in the dark...'

'It's possible. McGowan is known for inhabiting the Burns character even when they're not filming. I can just see him striding out on a moonlit walk.' She caught the note of sarcasm in her own tone and knew, from Sue's raised eyebrow, that she'd heard it too. 'The Captain's Eye,' Shona hurried on, 'where Vincent was found, is supposed to be haunted by the ghost of a smuggling captain who went down with his ship on the rocks.'

Professor Kitchen leaned forward, her hands clasped in front of her and her expression serious. 'Have you considered you may also be experiencing hyper-vigilance yourself?'

Shona had the sensation she was one of the professor's students who'd just made a page-one error.

'I'm a cop. Comes with the job,' Shona said, a little taken aback.

'You're a cop who's just mentioned ghosts,' the professor replied. 'The evidence in this case seems to be straightforward. If it walks like a duck, or in this case floats like a goose…'

Shona sighed and rolled her eyes. 'Honestly, Sue, if you'd seen what I saw, you wouldn't be making jokes like that.'

'Doctors use dark humour all the time. It's one way we cope with traumatic experiences.' Her expression remained serious, and her gaze never wavered from Shona. 'It's not just this sudden death, is it? What's really going on?'

Shona swirled the last of the coffee in her paper cup and, skewered by Sue's question, knew that this time there was no escape.

'The rape case against Delfont's been dropped by the CPS.'

Shona saw her friend's mouth settle into a hard line of disappointment and anger.

'There's more. A woman's come forward claiming new evidence in Rob's case, but he's been threatened, told not to appeal. The threat extends to me and Becca, and…' At the mention of her daughter's name, she felt her throat close up.

'You have to report this.' The professor's strong hand covered hers.

Shona shook her head, blinking back the tears. 'Prison doesn't work that way. The law doesn't count for much in there. Or outside, it seems.'

'There's no other way forward, Shona. Unless you take action, nothing will change.'

Shona looked down at the table. 'I know, I've tried. I've been through all of Rob's papers, looking for appeal grounds. With the rape charges dropped, even though there's video evidence of the assaults, for fuck's sake, how can I get this guy?' She cleared her throat, swallowing down the emotion that gripped her. 'Every time I go to work, or go out on the lifeboat, I know I'm taking my chances. With Becca it's different. Maybe Rob's right, we don't have a choice.'

'Does Becca know about the threats?' Sue said.

Shona nodded.

'And what does she think you should do?'

'Keep going after Delfont.'

Sue raised her eyebrows in a way that said *maybe you should listen to your daughter*.

'I know, Sue. But you're asking me to gamble with the lives of my husband and my daughter. That's not something I'm prepared to do. Not now. Not ever.'

Chapter 16

Filming was suspended. Partly as a mark of respect to Michael Vincent and partly due to the hasty scrabble to devise a new schedule. In the morning, Shona sat in a meeting room at the film production's Dumfries hotel base with Simon the director, writer Barry, James McGowan, Jan and a few other key crew members, all of them wondering if the whole project would collapse with the death of one of its main stars.

'We're gonnae finish this fuckin' film,' McGowan said, meeting the eye of everyone around the table, including Shona's, as if daring them all to contradict him. 'And we're gonnae make it a fitting memorial to Mikey.'

Shona thought it was the kind of red-carpet remark actors made when their main concern was their own bank balance. Simon conceded that most of Vincent's scenes were already in the can, but a new ending would need to be written. Shona saw Barry's shoulders droop as faces turned towards him.

'We'll need the whole plot rejigged by this afternoon,' McGowan said, cutting across Simon, and Barry's shoulders drooped further.

For the rest of that day and the next, Shona busied herself around High Pines. The birdwatching guests left, gratified by Shona's help, and posted a suitably glowing review that didn't actually mention mass bird deaths as a factor in their *perfect holiday*. The rooms were cleaned and reset. The improvement in Shona's ribs meant she could help Becca make the beds, and not be forced to lie down on them afterwards.

Becca had urged her mother to make the most of this brief, unexpected opportunity for rest, and Shona saw the sense of it. After lunch, she'd go upstairs and nap for an hour. From the bedroom windows she could see Tommy McCall at work on the *Ramsey Ranger*. Soon the yacht would be on her way back to the Isle of Man, and the whole episode would slide into memory, an anecdote and a warning, to be pulled out in the pub to entertain and chasten younger lifeboat members who thought they'd had a rough shout.

Shona kept in touch with her CID colleagues on progress on the house fire death and the warehouse arson cases. A pub landlord had come forward and told them he'd chased a couple of fellas for trying to flog iPads on his premises just before Christmas and CCTV was being viewed. Taylor Nicolson's birth father, Joe Dylan, having alibied his way out of his ex-partner's fatal house fire, now found himself in the frame for the warehouse insurance job.

Shona reviewed the statements and re-interviewed some of the film crew. But they offered little new information. She passed Professor Kitchen's findings on the alcohol in Vincent's stomach to director Simon Jones, who issued a warning of immediate dismissal to the entire company for anyone found with booze on set.

With Kate's help and a few calls to London's Metropolitan Police, where Vincent had lived, Shona established there was no credible intelligence to suggest the actor had debts with a criminal gang. He was, however, a person of interest in a high-class dealing operation and, had he lived, he'd likely have faced arrest and a custodial sentence.

In the current climate, would that have been enough to end his career? Shona didn't think so. Movie stars had come back from worse. He'd have done rehab, founded a charity, written his autobiography in prison and, very likely, emerged more marketable than before.

Either way, these new revelations tipped the balance towards suicide as a verdict. Not everyone planned to kill themselves – sometimes it was just impulse – but unless a note was uncovered, they'd never know for sure. Perhaps that was how Michael Vincent had wanted it.

Becca, energised by her chat with Barry and witnessing Robert Burns in swashbuckling action, had bashed out an essay in record time. Sitting on the corner sofa in the top-floor lounge, the night before filming was due to restart, Shona picked up a text from Ravi's partner, Martin, to say the essay was probably the most interesting thing he'd ever read about Scotland's national bard. Alarm bells ringing, Shona hastily checked over the attachment and found not a libellous tell-all of life on the film set, but a coherent argument for the role of literature in political change. Looking up from her laptop to see Becca lying on the floor, singing along to the theme tune of *SpongeBob SquarePants*, Shona wondered for the hundredth time in her daughter's life who this changeling was. A tiny spider could provoke hysterical screaming, but being in the middle of a pitched battle with gunfire and swords was just fine. She'd quickly adapted to the potential threat posed by Delfont, making sure she and her mother knew each other's whereabouts at all times. Slasher Sue was right. Becca was tougher and more resourceful than Shona sometimes gave her credit for. But at times she was still a little girl, who was worried about her dad. They both were.

Perhaps it was the evidence of how Becca was coping, or the chat she'd had with Sue, that had reignited her resolve to fight Delfont. Or maybe even that comment by Barry about films being shot out of sequence, the full story not being evident until it was all edited together. She knew what he meant. How many times had she looked at the elements of a crime – witness statements, forensic reports, alibis – jumbled into non-sequential order? A good detective would be continually revaluating, replacing, reframing, reordering the elements of the case until the true, coherent narrative – the truth – emerged.

But it was DS Thalia Brookes's most recent call that had tipped the balance. Her fellow victim in the case against DCI Harry Delfont had heard, unofficially, from an officer at Operation Vita what had prompted the CPS to drop the prosecution. The third victim, distressed by the delays in the case coming to court, had taken her own life with an overdose. Shona bitterly laid the woman's death squarely at Delfont's door. He was still ruining lives and would go on doing so until someone stopped him.

The final nail in the case's coffin had been, as Shona suspected, Rob's conviction. It undermined Shona's credibility as a witness. Despite the video evidence, the defence might claim Shona was having an affair with her boss and engaged in kinky sex to blackmail him into dropping investigations into her husband's crimes. The grubby sex lives of top city cops would get headlines, but it wouldn't get convictions. Two out of three victims were either dead or discredited; the CPS had cut their losses.

Thalia had felt guilty that she hadn't somehow foreseen Delfont's attack and Shona had told her she shouldn't. In turn, Thalia told Shona she mustn't feel guilty that Rob's conviction had undermined the case. But here they were, two victims burdened with misplaced guilt, while the man culpable for the attacks, and much more besides, escaped conviction and carried no guilt at all. Shona felt a white-hot spark of injustice re-ignite and this time the flame burned strong and steady.

Without consulting Rob, Shona had called Anoushka and asked her to pursue what Katherine Jones – Rob's former colleague – had to say about the money laundering.

Shona couldn't change the past but she was going to make damn sure that the future, especially her precious daughter's, wasn't blighted by having to look constantly over her shoulder. Slasher Sue was right: if she didn't act, nothing would change. It was going to be down to her to see this through to the end.

Chapter 17

The next day, when filming resumed, Shona watched Becca, in a maid's long skirt and linen shirt costume, make her entrance and exit the hall in Hildan House. The mood was subdued. The script had been hastily rewritten by Barry and this was the last scene due to be filmed on the island. Nobody appeared sad about leaving the place.

Lilly Chase stood, talking with a seated James McGowan. Shona crossed to join them and confirmed the actors' plans to return to their production base at the Dumfries hotel, and that security was in place.

'Will you send a car tonight?' McGowan glanced up at Shona.

She frowned. 'You want a uniform car to come to the hotel and check on you?'

McGowan looked equally confused. 'The Burns Supper? I can get Matt from security to drive me.'

'That would be best,' Shona agreed, suddenly aware that she'd forgotten all about the text she'd sent him with Amanda Collins's contact details and the expectation of a signed memento at best. Having made the invitation, she could hardly now ban him, and the small private gathering didn't pose any additional security risk. With a sinking heart, she realised the brief appearance she'd hoped to make at the supper would now be extended for as long as McGowan chose to stay.

Shona looked at Lilly, wondering if she should invite her too. Her security detail certainly wouldn't welcome this last-minute change of plan.

Lilly caught her look. 'I know what you're thinking, honey, but I don't have a thing to wear.'

What would a suitable Lilly Chase's Burns Night outfit look like? Shona wondered. Tartan PVC crinoline and unicorn hat? A dress made of actual haggis?

Lilly placed her hands on McGowan's shoulders. 'Anyway, it's Burns Night, clue is in the title. It's not Jean Armour night. I wouldn't want to steal your thunder, bro.' She bent down and gave him a theatrical kiss on the cheek. 'I'll just be home with my knitting, and my conference call to the Superbowl producers.'

James took her hand. 'Still flying back tomorrow? Must ye abandon me in ma hour of need?'

'I'm not forsaking ye, ma dearie,' Lilly replied, hand still in his and Jean Armour accent firmly in place.

Filming of Lilly's scenes was complete, and Shona had seen from the schedule sheet that the star was booked on an afternoon flight from Prestwick, only ninety minutes up the road from Dumfries, the next day.

'Sorry.' McGowan appeared to notice Shona was still there. 'See you later, DI Oliver.'

Shona felt a stab of irritation at the way he'd ignored and then dismissed her. Was that all it was? The jarring thought hit that a tiny part of her still held on to the connection she believed they'd once had. She wasn't jealous of his familiarity with Lilly, she told herself. It was nothing more than the last flickering of her childish crush being snuffed out and forgotten.

–

Shona hurried into the lounge at High Pines, wearing a black velvet cocktail dress with a full skirt that she referred to as her ceilidh dress. The neckline was cut high enough that her boobs wouldn't fall out of it, and the skirt had sufficient weight to spin without showing off her knickers. She began pulling open the doors of the pale oak sideboard.

'What you lookin' for, Mum?' Becca said, not taking her eyes off her laptop. Behind her, the deep windows showed the dark expanse of the firth and the small scattering of lights from the village below.

'Where's that tartan flower thingy?' Shona said, levering out another drawer and rifling through papers. 'Shut the curtains, will you?'

'We never shut the curtains.'

Shona stopped what she was doing and marched to the window, pulling on the heavy drapes. 'Sure you won't come with me tonight?'

'No way. Everyone there'll be about a hundred years old, and why are you being weird about the curtains?' Becca dragged her attention away from the music video and twisted around to look at her mother. Shona saw realisation dawn in her daughter's eyes. 'You're worried that man has got someone watching us. That's why you want me to come with you.'

'You don't have to come... The curtains... It's just to be on the safe side. Here, help me look for the flower thing,' Shona said, moving the conversation quickly on. 'I had it last Burns Supper, when I went with your dad.'

She felt a stab of grief. It had been the wrong thing to say.

But Becca showed no reaction and simply got up from the corner sofa. She pulled a small box from the sideboard and opened it to reveal a rosette in the red Oliver tartan. 'Next year, you and dad'll be going together,' she said quietly.

Shona felt the familiar clenching in her stomach whenever she was faced with Becca's hope. 'Yes, you're right,' she said brightly, not allowing any other thought to take root. She hugged Becca. 'Lock the doors while I'm out. I'll phone you when I'm on my way back.'

Shona arrived at the Caledonian Hotel a little before seven p.m. The windows in the sandstone three-storey façade of Scottish baronial turrets blazed with coloured lights that reflected off the wet flagstones, adding a festive air to the dreich night. A small group of fans waited by the main entrance, in danger of spilling from the narrow pavement into the path of passing buses. A couple of older men who didn't fit the profile of either Chasers or McGowan followers also stood nearby, cameras tucked beneath the open front of their waterproof jackets.

Shona swore under her breath as she approached the chaos. Two doormen were doing their best to contain the fans, but they were hopelessly outgunned. She pulled out her phone and called the control room, who promised to send a couple of Specials down, then texted McGowan: *Advise you enter CH via back door.*

Struggling through the throng, Shona flashed her warrant card at the doormen. In the foyer, the chair of the B&B group, Amanda Collins, stood in her emerald floor-length silk gown and plaid shoulder sash, flanked by committee members and a piper in full regalia, like a queen receiving her guests. Shona wished she had Murdo with her – part back-up, part Burns Supper guide – despite his avowed disgust of vegetarian haggis, which McGowan had stipulated for his address.

'Mr McGowan will be here in a minute,' Shona said, as Amanda leaned forward to deposit a chilly peck on her cheek.

'Never doubted you for a moment,' she replied, as if Shona had passed some personal test of character. 'Do go through. I've seated you beside the Frasers.'

Shona walked down the short hallway, past the chafing dishes holding the haggis, neeps and tatties, and popped her head into the dining room. A long table ran the full length, laden with candles and flowers, and with guests already seated down each side. Shona saw a card with McGowan's name on it at the top of the table, next to Amanda's and adjacent to her coterie of particular friends. A second, smaller trestle had been placed at right angles to the table's head. This is where the haggis would be addressed at the beginning of the supper, the most honoured guest getting the best view. Hugh and Janet Fraser, who owned a small B&B in Annan, waved to Shona from the other end of the room, next to the fire exit, and pointed to the seat beside them.

Shona heard a flurry of excited whispers from the waiters and waitresses lined up ready behind her, and returned to the foyer as McGowan, dressed as Robert Burns – in a long, dark velvet coat, an embroidered waist-coat, breeches and high boots – strode into view. He shook hands with the committee, his face serious. For one excruciating second, Shona thought Amanda Collins was going to curtsey, but she moderated the action to a gracious bow of her head.

An official group photograph was taken, McGowan impatient, as if this modern intrusion impinged on his habitation of Robert Burns. The hotel manager came forward and indicated a large vegetarian haggis on a side table. McGowan urged the committee to take their seats and Shona took her own at the bottom end of the table.

When all was ready, the piper led the way as McGowan entered, carrying the haggis on a great silver platter. There were whoops and cheers from the diners. They got to their feet and stamped and clapped in time to the pipe tune 'Scotland the Brave', as the honoured, grey-brown delicacy was paraded on a circuit of the room.

James McGowan turned on the charm, smiling and nodding to the B&B owners, who beamed back at one of Scotland's most famous Hollywood sons come home, although most would be hard-pressed to name any of his blockbuster movies. It was almost as if Robert Burns himself had returned in the flesh and they felt themselves to be among the blessed, which, being such pillars of the community and hospitality entrepreneurs, was only their due.

When the haggis had completed the circuit, McGowan placed the tray on the trestle. A reproduction of the famous portrait of Burns, produced in oils by painter Alexander Nasmyth, hung on the panelling behind. Shona had to admit, the likeness to McGowan was uncanny.

Glasses of whisky arrived, one for the piper and one for McGowan. He picked his up, turned to the kilted man in a toast of thanks for his playing. There was a round of appreciative applause. Both men downed their drams in one and shook hands. McGowan faced the diners and waited until they'd sat down, and silence had fallen on the room.

'It's difficult to overstate what the name Robert Burns means to me,' McGowan began. 'Other countries have their great poets or great songwriters, or individuals who collected all the melodies of a nation or gave the wisest sayings in their mother tongue and laid them down for posterity. Here in Scotland, one man did all this, which makes Robert Burns a singular individual.'

There were appreciative grunts and taps on the tables in response.

'As a poet, he wrote some marvellous work, as we'll hear here tonight. As a songwriter, he gave us the second-most-sung song in the world after "Happy Birthday".' He turned to one of the nearby diners, a barrel-chested and ruddy-faced man in full kilt and dress jacket, and said in a stage whisper, 'I'm talking about "Auld Lang Syne" for those of you who're not allowed out at Hogmanay.' The man laughed, and his diminutive wife sat beside him nodded and glowed with pleasure at the joke.

'So, Robert Burns was a remarkable guy,' McGowan continued. 'It's why I chose to make the film here, in his adopted home town of Dumfries. I can see why he loved it. Never seen so many bonnie lassies.' He flashed a smile that ran the length of the table, coming to rest on Shona. His gaze remained a moment longer, then he winked at her. Suddenly, she saw a flash of the old Jazza. She felt herself redden. 'And he did write the following. The "Address to a Haggis".'

The diners sat up straight, called to attention by the gravity of the moment, the highlight of the evening. It heralded, for some, the imminent arrival of their dinners, and for others the point when it might be respectable to begin downing a few drams.

'Fair fa' yer honest, sonsie face,' McGowan began, then raised his arms and flexed his muscles, adopting a body-builder pose. 'Great chieftain o' the puddin-race.' There was a ripple of appreciative laughter, particularly from the female members of the audience. There he was again, Jazza as Shona remembered him. Although perhaps, as an actor, he'd claim this was how Burns, rockstar of his day and always with an eye for the ladies, would have delivered his address to the haggis. But it was the height of shite, Shona told herself. A pure gallus act. She'd seen what an arse he really was.

McGowan continued to praise the virtues of the haggis, then grasped the polished ox-horn handle of the sgian-dubh that lay on the white tablecloth next to the salver.

'His knife see rustic Labour dight, An' cut you up wi' ready sleight…'

McGowan held the blade above his head then plunged it into the haggis.

There was a loud crack. A spurt of red sprayed in a high arc across McGowan, the white cloth and the guests at the top of the table. Scarlet smoke began to fill the room. There was a moment of shocked silence and then a woman screamed. Shona was already on her feet. Guests stumbled back in panicked confusion.

Shona turned and, with a sharp lunge that made her ribs squeal in protest, thrust open the fire door. 'Out,' she yelled, above the ringing alarm. 'All of you. Out!'

She pushed against the tide of kilts and highland plaids, crouching low to avoid the worst of the smoke. As she reached McGowan, she caught a whiff of garlic but a second later realised it wasn't from the food, but the unmistakable smell of tear gas. Shit. Shit. Shit. She grabbed a cloth napkin and held it to her nose and mouth, pulling the actor to the ground as she did so. The piper and the waiting staff had fled out the door into the foyer.

McGowan was spluttering, his face, high white collar and neckerchief stained blood-red. She searched his skin, then pulled at the knot of his neckerchief, trying to find the wound. Her finger immediately reddened in a way that told her he wasn't covered in slippery, viscous blood, but dye.

'Are you hurt? Can you walk?' Shona said, tying the napkin around her face like a bandit and grabbing one for McGowan. She glanced over her shoulder at the haggis, which still sat on the salver, a volcano of red smoke pouring from the midst of it.

'I'm okay, I think.' He struggled to his knees, coughing, and Shona tied the napkin over his face as she also began to feel the effects of the tear gas. She pulled his arm around her shoulders and heaved him to his feet. His weight against her conjured a muscle-memory that, for the briefest moment, sent her flying back to the Garthamlock playground of their shared past.

But then everything vanished in the scramble for safety. A stiff breeze from the open fire door was whipping the smoke into frenzied ghostly shapes, vivid spectres in the candlelight. Her eyes streamed. She heard McGowan wheeze beneath his makeshift mask as they stumbled towards the fire door. Ahead were blue lights and wailing sirens. As she dragged him forward, McGowan began to recover and became less of a burden on her shoulders.

They reached the door and almost fell down the step that led out onto the terrace. Each pulled their napkin mask free and gulped the cold air as if they'd surfaced from the depths of the ocean. Amid the blur of bodies, the night lit up, blinding white. The cameras had caught them. James McGowan, Hollywood star, his clothes claret-red and his face an apparently bloody mask – and, beneath his arm, shoring him up, his rescuer DI Shona Oliver.

She turned to look at him. White fire danced in her blurred vision, but one thing she was completely clear about. Whatever had happened tonight, there could be no question: James McGowan was the target.

Chapter 18

Shona set off early for McGowan's hotel the next morning. Last night, once he'd been taken to hospital, she'd returned to the scene and stayed until the early hours. An explosives team had arrived from the MOD firing range at Dundrennan to check the area was safe before the fire service and forensics got to work. McGowan's injuries were the most serious, but a few of the older guests were kept in at the infirmary overnight, suffering from the effects of the tear gas and shock. The dye wouldn't wash off either clothes or skin, and Shona could feel her newly elevated popularity with the B&B owners' committee plummeting once more.

Although Shona had called Amanda Collins to check she was okay, and to offer a direct number for the uniform liaison officer or any assistance required, the voicemail messages she'd left had remained resolutely unanswered. Well, if that was her attitude, she could bolt, as far as Shona was concerned. She had bigger things to worry about, namely who was targeting James McGowan, and why.

As Shona drew into the hotel carpark, she tutted at the fans and press who'd already gathered. Before she could get out of the car, Kate rang with further updates from forensics and she jotted them down in her notebook.

When the call ended, her phone buzzed again, and she was surprised to see DC Dan Ridley's name flash up.

'Just checking everything's okay. Saw you on the news.'

The cross-border element of policing formed a significant part of Shona's remit, with her patch abutting Cumbria, in England, to the south. Dumfries and Galloway also contained one of the main arterial routes from Europe to Northern Ireland in the west, across the twelve miles of what was colloquially known as the narrow sea. Relationships with other forces were important, and so Dan had become more friend than colleague over the course of previous inquiries.

'I'm fine,' Shona said. She'd seen the front pages of some of the tabloids already – *Burns Night went with a bang for Hollywood star James McGowan as pranksters cooked his haggis extra spicy*. 'State of me in those photos, though.'

'Well, it does look like you and James McGowan are stumbling out of a nightclub after a particularly lethal round of cocktails,' Dan said. 'Caught red-handed, eh?'

'Stop. I'm mortified,' Shona said. 'That's my best ceilidh dress ruined.'

'He owes you a new frock. Multi-millionaire, right? Get the Gucci catalogue out.'

She felt her spirits lift a little at the gentle teasing. Slasher Sue was right, sometimes a dose of dark humour was the only way to momentarily lighten the load.

'You're both okay, though?' Dan's voice turned serious. 'Must have been tough.'

Shona looked at her red-stained hands, and something in that small statement of fellow-feeling opened a door she'd been holding closed since the night before. All cops had them: jobs that stamped marks on you as indelible as the dye on her hands.

'I was on autopilot last night. Training kicked in, I suppose,' Shona said quietly. 'But just for a moment when I got outside, all the shocked faces, red everywhere. The smoke and the blue lights, and the weight of someone on my shoulder, it took me back to 7/7.'

The London bombings, 7 July 2005. Suicide bombs exploded on three underground trains and a bus. Shona had gone with uniform colleagues to Aldgate Tube station in the City of London and helped tend to the injured and traumatised commuters, some of whom just sat on the pavement, stained by the blood of strangers and incapable of speech or further movement.

'These things creep up on you, don't they?' said Dan. 'Good thing that nobody was badly hurt last night.'

Shona shook the images of London streets from her head. 'Yes. True. McGowan has burns to his hands, and staining from the dye, but he's otherwise okay. I'm on my way to interview him now.'

'Good luck,' Dan said. 'Oh, by the way, we're investigating a couple of cases of counterfeit iPads catching light. Might be linked to your fatal house fire. We're looking into a possible supply route.'

'Sounds promising. Can you bell Murdo and let him know?' Shona fished her bag from the passenger seat and got out her warrant card, ready to show the constable at the hotel entrance. 'Everything okay with you?' she said, knowing it sounded like an afterthought. 'Come over for lunch one Saturday, bring...' She stopped, unable to retrieve Dan's girlfriend's name. Jewellery designer. Made Becca's bracelet. God, what was her name?

'Charlotte and I are having a break,' Dan said. 'But it's fine.'

'Oh, okay.' Shona thought he sounded a little down. He and his girlfriend had been together six months, and it had still been fairly casual, with work pressures on both sides, but Dan had seemed quite taken with Charlotte Rutter. Perhaps they'd make up. 'So come anyway,' Shona said brightly, hoping to push back the momentary gloom. 'Becca would love to see you. I'd love to see you. Sorry, I've really got to go.' Shona pulled on the door handle and a blast of icy air and noise from the road filled the car. 'Thanks for the call, Dan. And I mean it, come soon.'

She slid her phone into her coat pocket and bowed her head, partly against the wind but mostly to avoid being recognised by any of the waiting photographers. She'd abandoned the jeans and fleece of the last few days for a charcoal grey business suit which she thought made her suitably anonymous, but she'd only gone a few steps when one of the fans called out to her.

'Detective Shona!' It was the fan in the crop top she'd encountered outside the Robert Burns House museum. It seemed she'd neither succumbed to exposure nor acquired more weather-appropriate clothing. 'Is James okay?' Crop-Top called.

'A statement has been issued,' Shona said, one eye on the journalists. 'I've nothing to add.'

'Are you seeing him now? Tell him we love him. Tell him we're thinking about him,' the girl cried, setting off a chorus of similar calls. Hands tried to thrust flowers, cards and soft toys into Shona's arms, but she signalled for one of the set security men-in-black to come forward and do the honours.

'Any nearer to catching the pranksters, DI Oliver?' a male voice with an English accent called above the racket.

'Are haggis safe to approach, or should the public be on their guard?'

There were sniggers in the crowd. It was on the tip of her tongue to make a quip about vegetarian haggis being less feisty than their free-range cousins, but she knew he was trying to entice her into making just such a throwaway comment. She wasn't about to trivialise what had happened or imply that the police weren't taking it seriously. Instead, Shona remained light-lipped, and merely rolled her eyes.

'How's your husband liking the food in his new establishment?' called another voice. 'Five stars, is it?'

It took all her self-control not to round on the heckler.

Instead, she continued to the hotel door. Rob's conviction was going to follow her around like a bad smell. She could only pray Detective Superintendent Davies didn't get wind of it. If the constable heard the remark, he had the good sense not to show it. He merely glanced at her warrant card and ushered her inside.

Chapter 19

Matt from security opened the hotel room door. Shona gave a look devoid of any approval. The blame for the previous evening's incident hardly lay with him, but neither had he distinguished himself by his conduct after the blast either. Shepherding the waitresses to safety was a point in his favour, but he'd left McGowan to take his chances in a smoke-filled room.

She took a deep breath and went down the suite's short hallway, past a neat bedroom and bathroom, into an over-heated sitting room equipped with two sofas and a massive TV. A well-thumbed copy of *The Collected Works of Robert Burns* – coloured Post-it tags protruding from its pages – lay on the coffee table. McGowan himself sat on a rose-patterned sofa that, if anything, highlighted his newly acquired complexion. His cheek had a streaked red patch and his eyes were still swollen from the tear gas. Both hands were covered in non-adherent dressings, with the right, which had wielded the knife, more heavily bandaged. According to forensics, the dye also contained an even longer-lasting, invisible component. Under an ultraviolet lamp, he'd light up like a purple Christmas tree.

He was surprisingly composed. Filming, already behind schedule, was suspended until the dye wore off. She'd expected him to be incandescent and had considered, only half-jokingly, bringing a police dog with her in order to subdue him.

He welcomed her with a small nod. 'DI Oliver. How you doin' today?'

She'd usually invite victims to call her Shona, but he hadn't asked to be called James, so she didn't bother. The brief intimacy she'd felt, conjured by the previous night's rescue, had vanished.

'I'm well,' she said. 'And you?'

'No' bad.' He held up his hands and indicated his face. 'Been worse. Been better.'

He seemed quiet, controlled. Maybe the hospital kept a tranquiliser rifle under the counter and had darted him. If so, the effects hadn't quite dissipated.

'All the other guests are fine, by the way,' Shona said, thinking, but not adding, *in case you're interested*.

'Oh aye, I was just about to ask,' McGowan said. 'Maybe I can send them something?'

'Flowers?' Shona said, archly.

'I was thinking an invitation to the film's premiere.'

After last night, Shona thought, most of them will have had enough of Robert Burns to last a lifetime. He didn't seem to require an answer from her so Shona sat down on the sofa opposite and took out her notebook. 'The hospital will have told you your injuries were caused by an exploding security dye pack.'

'Aye. No' really sure what that is.'

'They were first used in banks in the 1990s, hidden in wads of notes to cover the thief in what they call safety ink, but more correctly it's a reactant chemical marked as Disperse Red 9. Now it's mostly tracking devices, but three-quarters of US banks still use them, so they're widely available.'

Kate had given her a full rundown, supplementing what she'd initially been told by forensics the night before.

'Some, like the one that detonated last night, also contain tear gas,' Shona continued. 'Usually, there's a timer, or radio signal receiver, but stabbing one with a sgian-dubh probably counts as tampering, and that set it off.' She gave him a small smile, then her expression turned serious. 'You were lucky. The detonation creates a temperature of around two hundred degrees. There was real danger of burns.'

'Aye well, maybe they just can't resist a pun.' James grinned, but Shona didn't indulge him, and his smile quickly faded. 'So, who has access to stuff like that?' he asked.

'They're used in ATMs, vending machines and, I'm told, some delivery drivers like Amazon and even Deliveroo are carrying them to deter thieves. But I was hoping you'd have some idea who targeted you and why?'

He shook his head, but then stopped. 'I got a note yesterday – U will dye. Ye know, D, Y, E. I thought it was a joke. Just bad spelling.'

'And you didn't tell me?'

'Like I said, it didnae mean anything to me.'

'D'you still have it?' Shona frowned.

'Mibbaes. Came with some fan stuff. Was waiting when I got back from Hildan Island.' He looked vaguely around the room, then at a table piled high with cards and gift boxes, some opened, some untouched.

Shona made a note. 'I'd appreciate if you didn't open anything else until we've checked it.' She'd already decided the material coming from fans would need to be sifted for suspicious items and had asked uniform for a couple of forensically trained constables or Specials.

She'd also actioned the resultant social media posts and given Kate the unenviable job of ploughing through those, aided by Chloe and Vinny Visuals, for anything that might either indicate a motive or point to a perpetrator.

'Tell me about the issues you had with the Arctic Guardians,' Shona said.

McGowan let out a loud breath. 'It's like Simon told you. Northgoose came in on a film set in the Arctic. We were ten days from the shoot and $100K short. They kitted all the crew out, as well as investing some cash.' He shrugged. 'Truth is, if they hadnae stepped in the whole project would've collapsed. It was just clothes. We werenae slaughtering wildlife for the film. The hoops we jump through on animal safety these days mean you're probably safer being a horse on set than an actor.'

'If you were a horse, it'd make my job easier.' Shona couldn't resist the jibe. 'Stick you in a stable with a bucket of water and some hay.'

'You say that, but then look at what happened with Shergar,' he said, referring to the racehorse stolen for ransom by an armed gang in 1983, and never seen again.

'True,' she conceded with a small smile. 'If you were a horse, I'm sure you'd cause just as much trouble.'

She was surprised when he looked a little crestfallen, and she regretted her tone.

'Now, getting back to the matter in hand, the Northgoose clothing company is the only reason AG targeted you?'

'Aye, seems like it,' McGowan said with a weary shake of his head.

It certainly tallied with what Kate had dug up. Although the group were mostly active in the US and didn't have any record with explosives, there was always the possibility of a rogue individual frustrated with the group's non-violent approach. However, this felt more personally malicious, and while it was a public act, a bunch of elderly B&B owners were not the type of audience to record the incident on their phones and send the footage viral.

'Listen, do you mind if we get some coffee?' McGowan said. 'I've been up all night.' Shona blinked at him. 'And I'm sure you have been too,' he added hastily.

Okay, perhaps he retained a scrap of empathy, but it would be nice, Shona thought, if he didn't need to be reminded other people existed.

'Fine, let's do that,' Shona said. He remained seated, so she got up to find Matt, who was slouched by the suite door scrolling through his phone.

'So, beyond the note with the bad spelling, there's no specific fans that worry you?' Shona said, when she'd returned to her seat opposite McGowan.

'Nope.'

'Whoever did this wasn't messing about. After you went to hospital, I had to call in the bomb squad.'

'Why?' He looked genuinely mystified.

'Because of the possibility of a secondary device. It's a common tactic. First explosion is small, attracts bystanders or someone rushes in to put out the fire, and then a more destructive device is detonated. Guess what we found?'

She locked eyes with him. He was the first to look away.

'We found an improvised explosive device,' she said. 'That's an IED to you. It's a miracle it didn't detonate, but if it had, you'd have probably lost your hand, maybe your eyesight too.' She'd been purposely callous in telling him, but she wanted to shock McGowan out of his complacency. When the geese had died from bird flu, he'd been convinced he was a target. Now something had happened to him, he seemed oblivious to the danger he might be in.

'When you were in the hallway at the Caledonian Hotel, did you see anyone or anything that concerned you?' she said, raising her pen ready to record his reply, as if this action in itself might prompt his recollection.

They'd interviewed the staff and the hotel manager, who'd admitted there were various points during the evening when the haggis, and specifically the vegetarian one reserved for McGowan to use in his address, were left unattended. The actor's arrival had drawn the staff down to watch, and also when the official photographs were taken. Shona felt the switch must have been done later rather than earlier in the evening to minimise the chance of accidental detonation, or of someone noticing the change.

They were interrupted by the sound of the suite door opening, the coffee arriving. And with it, the unmistakable entry of Lilly Chase.

'James, you look like shit,' she called as she approached Shona, who got up and offered her hand. Lilly launched herself forward. For a split second, Shona tensed, wondering if Lilly blamed her for the attack on her co-star and friend, but the diminutive singer just hugged her fiercely, then said into her ear, 'You are a fucking queen.'

Letting go of a startled Shona, she said, 'James, this woman is a fucking queen. She saved your sorry Scottish ass.'

McGowan opened his mouth, but she cut him off. 'Hey, hey, I'm talkin' here. I hope you thanked her, and not just flowers, baby. I hope you thanked her on your knees.'

James slid from the sofa onto his knees and clasped his hands in front of him. Shona stared at him in horror.

'I truly and heartily thank you, DI Oliver,' he chanted, then, more genuinely, 'I mean it. Thank you.'

'And you promise to name all your future children after her, even the boys?'

'Especially the boys,' James said, obediently.

Shona tried not to show the satisfied amusement she felt at Lilly's ability to put McGowan so firmly in his place.

'Okay, you can get up,' Lilly replied, throwing herself onto the sofa and crossing one platform boot over another. She waved away Matt's offer of coffee as he placed cups in front of McGowan and Shona.

'Any idea who was behind it?' Lilly asked, after Matt had returned to the hallway. 'This wasn't just a prank like the media are making out, was it?'

'No, it wasn't,' Shona said, and sipped her coffee, watching McGowan.

Something in his demeanour had changed since Lilly's arrival. His responding glance to Shona seemed to be a tacit signal that he was ready to co-operate. She'd arrived like a tornado, but Shona felt McGowan wanted to protect his co-star from the worst. Perhaps that was to make sure she wasn't put off working with him in the future or promoting the film. Or maybe he just didn't want her leaving with the impression that his home country was more dangerous than downtown LA. It suited Shona to have him more compliant, and not to mention the IED. The fewer people who knew about that, the better. The last thing she wanted was copycats, fan hysteria or a heads-up to the assailant.

'You think this is connected to Michael's death?' Lilly shot McGowan an apologetic glance. 'I'm sorry, honey, but wouldn't you rather know? It ain't your fault he went out in your coat.'

'At this stage,' Shona began carefully, 'there's nothing to indicate the incidents are connected.'

'Is that a yes or a no?' said Lilly, bluntly.

'It's a no,' Shona said, matching her directness. 'But I can't rule out that won't change if we find new evidence.'

'Like what?' Lilly countered.

'A previous attempt. Or a witness with new information.'

Lilly looked at McGowan, but he shook his head.

'So, what else?' Lilly turned back to Shona.

'Leaving aside the forced entry to your home in Hollywood,' Shona began, 'any previous issues with fans?'

'How long have you got?' McGowan said. 'Threatening letters. Turning up at my kids' school, offering to sell me a website in my own name.' He ticked each item clumsily off on his bandaged fingers. 'Someone tried to kidnap my ex-wife's dog. There's a fan with a five-year restraining order for stealing one of my shoes as a souvenir. But nothing like this.'

'Is it possible we're talking old enemies?' Shona said. 'Could your return to Scotland have stirred up any previous grudges for example?'

She saw a flash of something like recognition in his eyes, but it vanished as quickly as it had appeared. 'Naebody comes to mind.'

'Okay.' Shona consulted her notebook. 'And you've had no run-ins with any of the background artists or crew on the set?'

Again, McGowan shook his head.

Shona looked from McGowan to Lilly and back. 'I need to ask you about your personal life and your finances. Are you happy for Ms Chase to remain?'

'It's fine,' he said, slumping back on the sofa with a wave of his hand, 'Press on, Macduff.'

Shona consulted the notes Kate had given her, flicking to a page at the back. 'Tell me what happened with your agent, Bryson Drake?'

'We had a parting of the ways.'

'Why? Financial? Personal?'

'Bit of both.' McGowan leaned forward again, elbows on knees, and Shona saw the extent of the dye on his face, how it clung around his eyebrows and the day's growth of stubble. He suddenly looked less like a dynamic movie star and more like the victims of crime she normally encountered. Tired, worried, uncomprehending.

'The break with Bryson had probably been on the cards for a while,' he said. 'He's focused on the big franchises. Used to be an actor himself. Did a bit of everything before, even ran a goldmine in Cornwall years ago. I want to take my career in the direction of…' He paused. 'Quality, not quantity. More stage. There's less money for clients and agents in that.' He gave her a rueful smile.

'And your personal life?' Shona asked.

'No drama there,' he said. 'I'm single. Get on well with my ex, Samira. Love ma twins, Dove and Beau. They've just turned eight.'

Shona nodded. 'Just lastly… Red Sun Productions? I understand you withdrew from a film last year and the company went bankrupt?'

'My agent handled that. An all-action Robert the Bruce war film. Never fancied it. Been done. *Outlaw*

King. Braveheart. Not for me. Anyway, companies fold an' reopen. Not the big deal it seems.'

Might be a big deal to someone, Shona thought. People have committed assaults for less. The company name and the red dye seemed too much of a coincidence for her to be entirely happy the events were unconnected. It's the sort of act you might not claim credit for, but secretly revel in. Filming disrupted, public humiliation. The IED was a step too far, but who knew how angry the perpetrator was and how much they might have lost in the bankruptcy.

'Okay, thank you. I'll not keep you any longer,' Shona said, getting to her feet. 'We need to find you a more secure hotel. And the personal protection you have may not be as experienced as you need,' she added, not caring to drop her voice.

'You're a cop,' Lilly said. 'Bet your home security is good. James, she has the cutest B&B right on the water. You should move in there, take the whole place.' She turned to Shona. 'He'll pay you double. You can chuck your guests. How much d'you need to compensate them?'

'That won't be necessary,' she said before she could stop herself. She didn't want to admit there were currently no guests – chuckable or otherwise – to compensate.

'So it's settled.' Lilly didn't wait for Shona's agreement but jumped up from the sofa and turned to McGowan. 'I can lend you Ricardo and Benji until you're done. But I fucking want them back, asshole. You're coming home to LA after, aren't you? Bring them with ya then.'

She made Ricardo and Benji sound like a pair of designer guard dogs: Shona had to mentally check the names on her list of the singer's security detail to make sure they were, indeed, human.

Her initial reaction to Lilly's suggestion was a flat no. Leaving aside the history between her and the egotistical and crabbit Mr McGowan, moving the potential target of a sociopathic and vengeful stalker closer to Becca was not what she had in mind. But if Becca was already in the line of fire from another direction, wouldn't more security be a blessing in disguise? It was unethical and counterproductive to involve McGowan in her own perilous situation. On the other hand, Lilly Chase's operation had been smooth as silk, her staff the best that money could buy.

McGowan looked just as uncertain of the arrangement as Shona did. But before either could kick the idea firmly into touch, Lilly kissed James goodbye, then looped her arm through Shona's.

'Walk me out, Detective Inspector,' she said, propelling Shona alongside her into the hallway.

'James is one of the good guys, ya know?' Lilly said when they reached the corridor. 'He made sure all the female actors are getting the same rates as the guys – the background artists, too. Unequal pay is the industry norm, but it's like you're being told you're not as good, less fucking worthy of reward. Most producers aren't honest about it, but James is.' She squeezed Shona's arm then waved her goodbye. 'You'll like him once ya get to know him, sis.'

I already know him, Shona thought, as well as I'd ever want to, thank you very much.

Chapter 20

There seemed little point in going back to the CID office, so Shona headed for the A75 and the thirty-minute drive home. Although she felt less resentment towards DI Dalrymple now that she realised he wasn't trying to oust her, she had no desire to witness him sitting in her chair, physically and metaphorically.

James McGowan had promised to look for the note he'd received, and the constables who'd arrived to help him search through the gifts and cards sent by fans would call if they found anything.

Without a clear picture of who was targeting him and why, it was hard to create an offender profile, and even more so to plan strategies that neutralised the threat they posed. What was McGowan's assailant capable of? The incident with the haggis had the potential to seriously injure him. Why not just run him over? Or send the IED in with all the other fan mementos? McGowan always had a certain level of security around him. To pull off a stunt like that you needed confidence to pass unnoticed among so many people.

In a single-lane section, she came up behind a lorry bound for the ferry at Cairnryan and eased off on the Audi's gas. Many drivers were impatient when the dual carriageway was forced to narrow due to the route's rolling topography. The A75 was regularly monitored for speeding and dangerous overtaking, but she often welcomed the limitations. It allowed her conscious mind to sit back a little, leaving room for her unconscious to sift the facts of whatever case was most troubling her.

It seemed to Shona that for McGowan's assailant it was all about pulling strings, making people dance to their tune. Beyond the damage to the film, whoever did this wanted inside McGowan's head. Now every person, known or unknown, whom the actor encountered would be viewed by him as a potential threat. Like Rob in prison, she thought, and a catch somewhere below her heart made her draw in a deep breath.

McGowan's apparently laid-back reaction started to make sense to Shona. It was bravado. You could take the boy outta Glasgow, but you couldn't take Glasgow outta the boy. *See me, I'm pure dead brilliant and nane o' you bastards can touch me* was the gallus motto of every man in the city. Swaggering like you didn't care, so people couldn't see you were scared, made you less likely to be targeted, the logic went.

But it didn't mean the danger would go away. Neither Rob Oliver nor James McGowan was ever going to be free of the threats they faced, without her help. And if they weren't careful, their bravado might just get them killed.

Shona crested the hill at the top of the village just as a shaft of sunlight caught the smooth grey water of the firth, illuminating it like a landing strip guiding her home. She felt a huge rush of tension leave her and rolled her window down a fraction so the blast of Atlantic air could carry away the last of the stuffiness from the hotel room. A cup of decent coffee and she could look at this case afresh.

Becca was at the kitchen table, laptop out. She looked up in pleased surprise at her mother's return. 'Thought you'd be ages.'

'Nothing I can't do from home.' Shona kissed the top of her daughter's head, earning a swipe as Becca rearranged her hair. 'What on earth are you looking at?'

On the screen was a skull with a large hole above the forehead and a mass of smaller perforations, but it didn't quite have the typical pattern of a shotgun blast.

'It's skeletal evidence of the history of venereal syphilis,' Becca said over her shoulder as she continued to type. 'The holes are called *caries sicca* and are erosions of the cranial bone indicating the disease has reached the brain. Normally only seen on pre-antibiotics skeletons.'

'Hooray for penicillin,' Shona said. 'Is this work or pleasure?'

Becca stopped typing and screwed up her face like a child caught out skiving from her studies. 'Bit of both.'

'Okay, darling. Don't get too carried away with the dead people.'

'Look who's talking,' Becca muttered, pulling up a page of maths equations.

Shona suppressed a smile as she climbed up on the worktop to rummage about at the back of a high cupboard. She unearthed a small jar of coffee beans triumphantly from their hiding place.

'So that's where you keep your stash,' Becca said.

'Dad's secret stash,' Shona said. 'Promise you won't tell him. It's a caffeine crisis.' She tipped most of the jar's contents into the grinder and set it running.

'If you book me on the Antonine Wall dig I won't say a thing,' Becca yelled over the noise. 'They've found evidence of another Roman fortlet. That's a small fort.'

'You can dig in the garden,' Shona replied, filling the cafetière from the boiled kettle. 'I'll get some chicken bones from the Royal Arms off Freya and not tell you where I've buried them. How about that?' Shona grinned as she gathered cup and coffee up, and made for Rob's office across the landing.

'You'll end up in the garden if you keep this up,' Becca said under her breath.

'Heard that,' Shona called as she shut the door.

Shona took an aromatic mouthful, set her notebook on the desk and pulled up the contacts on her phone. Vanda McLeod answered, her quietly spoken Glaswegian voice betraying no surprise at Shona's call after a gap of over a year.

'Shona,' she said. 'How nice to hear from you. Is this professional or social?'

'Professional,' Shona said. 'But it's not to book a therapy session. I just need your advice with a case.'

Shona credited Vanda for helping her to deal effectively with the fallout from Delfont's attack. Despite there now being little prospect of a trial, the psychologist had saved her sanity and large parts of her life as she knew it.

'I have a gap now,' Vanda said. 'Fire away.'

'I want to talk to you about stalking,' Shona began. 'Can you give me an idea of the type of person I'm looking for?'

'Righto, well, in 50 per cent of cases it's an ex-partner and I don't have to tell you it's typically a gendered crime – male to female. About another third had prior contact with their stalker through work or friendships.'

'In this case it's a man,' Shona said. 'Specifically a celebrity. Does that make a difference?'

'I'll not ask you to break confidentiality, but I have seen the news, Shona,' Vanda said. 'Is this James McGowan we're talking about?'

'Since this is a professional consultation and I know I can trust you, yes, it is. And this wasn't a prank. It was only luck he avoided a potentially fatal injury.'

'Okay, in that case the attacker is most likely someone with low-level mental health problems who's struggling with difficulties in their life. They may be unemployed or under-employed. Typically, they fantasise a relationship to deal with it. We call it faux intimacy.'

'So, a perceived relationship means they've probably been in touch before?' Shona said, making a note. It might mean the culprit was already on the radar, either here or in the US.

'Yes, that's probable. Most stalkers don't move straight to exploding foodstuffs,' Vanda said. 'Seriously, I'd be looking for letters, calls, gifts. Any repeated attempts at contact. They may have created tribute sites or fan fiction. If they're active on message boards they'd be vocal about the special nature of their relationship.'

'I've met some fans like that already,' Shona said, remembering the almost religious devotion she'd encountered.

'The most common stalker is a former partner or someone who perceived a romantic rejection, and they can become violent if denied their desired outcome.'

There'd been no mention of this in Kate's briefing, and McGowan hadn't talked about any vengeful ex-girlfriend.

'Okay.' Shona made a note.

'But as I said, celebrities are mainly targeted by stalkers we'd call erotomaniac or intimacy seekers, who harbour a delusional belief there is already an intense relationship.

They can become vindictive and violent, even when there's been little contact, seeking to cause distress and damage their victim's reputation.'

'And these individuals are unlikely to stop of their own accord?' Shona asked.

'Very unlikely,' Vanda replied. 'This is not a crush scenario that fades with time or after interaction with the object of the crush, when reality triggers a reappraisal.'

After her recent interaction with McGowan, Shona thought ruefully, she agreed with that assessment.

Vanda's voice softened. 'We've all had crushes. It's why it's best sometimes not to meet your heroes.' She became serious again. 'There's generally an escalating pattern of behaviour that requires more intense interconnection to gain the same reward.'

'You make them sound like serial killers,' Shona said, the hairs on the back of her neck rising.

'There are certain differences,' Vanda mused. 'But it's not a bad comparison. Think of the man who shot John Lennon. He wanted his name connected to his icon in perpetuity and one way of doing it was to murder him.'

'Okay, thanks, Vanda. That's really helpful.'

'Anytime, Shona. And remember if you ever want to see me, just pop up.'

'Thank you, I will.'

Shona remained at the desk, pondering what Vanda had told her. She rested her chin on her hands, ignoring the view across the estuary from the window, eyes focused instead on the notes she'd made. Delusional. Vengeful. Violent.

She called Kate. 'I want the name of every fan outside the hotel, and I want them checked. Especially anyone who's previously been issued with a restraining order regarding McGowan. Where are they now? Get Vinny onto their social media if they have any. I want their mugshots.'

'The Hollywood stalker who crashed his house is definitely still in custody. You think it's another fan?'

'Main line of enquiry now,' Shona said. 'And the gifts left at the hotel. If there's anyone who's been bombarding McGowan with an unusual amount of presents, or multiple attempts at contact, give them special attention.'

As she ended the call, she caught sight of herself reflected in the window and realised what Lilly Chase had been doing in the hotel suite. She pictured the diminutive star, the blunt phrasing of her questions and how she'd mirrored Shona's body language. Lilly had probably been gathering audition material for the *British cop show* she'd mentioned when they first met. Shona found herself chuckling. She'd told Barry the scriptwriter she didn't watch cop shows, but if she was going to be immortalised by anyone, she'd be happy for it to be the fluently sweary, fabulously outrageous Lilly Chase.

–

After one of Becca's soup-and-roll working lunches, Shona called the agency that provided the extras for the film. She could have handed the job to Kate, but she seemed to be juggling enough. The agency claimed they vetted everyone who applied online or through the app. Prospective background artists needed a national insurance number and the appropriate right-to-work documents, and had to be over eighteen years old, except in special circumstances. Shona knew that wasn't true. Becca was only sixteen. Then again, she could have easily lied on her application, but in that case, they certainly hadn't checked her details. Rather than dob in her own daughter, Shona thanked them for their time and asked for a list of all the extras working on the film. The owner was reluctant, but when Shona told him it was in connection with a sudden death and that she'd easily get a warrant to examine all their business dealings, he changed his mind.

She'd been expecting Detective Superintendent Davies's call. When it finally came, he was suitably to the point. 'Are we classing this haggis incident as an attempted murder? Because if we're not, there's a lot of resources going into something that could just be a prank.'

'I'd rather nobody blew up James McGowan on our patch, sir.' She was just the right side of respectful. It was not like she was billing Police Scotland for her dress. 'We've had a few volunteers from uniform go over to his hotel and sift for evidence. It's not all going through the books. And he's taken steps for his own protection. It won't cost us a thing.'

She was tempted to refer to McGowan's potential move to High Pines as an 'in-house arrangement' but thought better of it. 'His company are considering moving him to my self-contained accommodation here, as we have excellent intruder deterrents. Lilly Chase has supplied two close protection staff from her own security detail.'

'I'm not sure that's appropriate,' Davies said uncertainly.

'I admit I wasn't keen at first, sir, but it makes sense.' She'd rationalised the potential awkwardness of the situation by reminding herself that the guest suites were separate, and she'd have no more contact with McGowan than was strictly necessary – and she'd be able to keep a closer eye on Becca.

'Ms Chase's people ran checks on us even before they got here. That's how thorough they are. Ex–Navy SEALs.' She wasn't sure if the last bit was true, but it seemed to impress Davies. 'Frankly, sir, we just need to keep a lid on this until the caravan moves on.'

The idea that it could soon be someone else's problem might do the trick.

'As to keeping a lid on things, we've had an approach from a journalist asking about your personal situation,' Davies said.

Shona's heart dropped, remembering the question shouted from the crowd outside the hotel. 'I hope you won't be responding, sir.'

'The quicker this is cleared up, the better for all of us. Keep me informed,' Davies said and ended the call.

He was making it clear he'd only defend her up to a point. After that she'd be on her own. If he knew she was planning to take on Delfont, and potentially reignite the whole scandal, he'd have suspended her on the spot.

'Mum,' Becca called from the kitchen. 'Why's the High Pines account gone up by ten grand?'

Shona frowned as she looked over her daughter's shoulder at the laptop screen. The payment was labelled BHP – Boat Hoose Productions. She had to admit, the figure was doing something for her uneasiness at having them here. It wasn't just a fee. It was breathing space for High Pines. But even at double rates, how long was he planning on staying? Shona was desperately trying to do the maths when the gate buzzer sounded.

She checked the video monitor. Two fourbies with blacked-out windows sat in the road. This time Shona wasn't worried. She recognised Lilly's security team and pressed the release.

'Becca, there are some guests I meant to tell you about. You might have to make some allowances for them. We both might.' After all, she thought, there can't be too many cases where part of the SIO's job is to make sure everyone has the right pillows.

Chapter 21

Lilly Chase's security detail – dubbed by her, Ricardo and Benji – turned out to be British. Very British. Ex-Special Forces.

Ricardo was a Richard from London, while Benji – who actually preferred Ben – was from a former mining village in Nottinghamshire. Both wore their hair tight-cropped and had a lean hardness that didn't look like it had been acquired solely in gyms. The weather was good in Hollywood, they said. The food was shit, and their clients mostly mad as bats, but they paid top dollar. Lilly Chase was, they said, a solid lass. Worked hard, no bullshit, and mostly did what she was told. No unscheduled walkabouts or drugs. Never let herself get within grabbing distance of fans, no matter how friendly they looked.

Shona thought that growing up in a tough New York neighbourhood and being a woman of small stature likely informed how she navigated physical risk in a way that their male clients might not consider. Becca was listening open-mouthed, obviously delighted by the new guests.

Ric and Ben did the rounds of High Pines's perimeter fencing, gates, doors and windows. They weren't 100 per cent happy about the guest suites being on the ground floor but there was no way they'd want 'the ladies' to give up their upper-floor bedrooms. Mr McGowan was tired and needed to rest. They'd be right next door to him, and anyone who made it up that cliff of a garden was welcome to take their chances. They'd brought their own grub, didn't plan on going out that night, and would keep the noise down. Shona was handed a walkie-talkie, in case they needed to contact her in an emergency, and told to lock the connecting door to the main house.

After her guests were settled, Shona left Becca to her studies and walked down to the lifeboat station. The light was on, and Tommy's van was parked outside. Freya would still be at work at the Royal Arms, and it would be a good chance to report the improvement in her ribs and ask him to put her back on the call roster.

'You've no' been passed fit by the doctor,' he said, pointing his pen at her. The table in the upstairs crew kitchen was littered with paperwork, which he'd been ploughing through, and Shona could tell it hadn't put him in the best of moods. Not great for the favour she was about to ask.

'Tommy, where d'you think that missing Zodiac from Hildan Island is?' she asked, putting a fresh tea in front of him.

He shrugged. 'It's possible someone took it fae the island and just sold it on. Fetch quite a bit and folk don't ask too many questions.'

'Both Matt and Simon say it was there in the evening.' Shona sipped her tea, studying the top of Tommy's thinning hair as he bent over his forms. 'What if it was just common or garden incompetence?'

He looked up. 'How d'you mean?'

'Wasn't tied up properly and just drifted. Where would it go?'

He shrugged again and when Shona didn't say anything, he sighed and got up, crossing into the neighbouring office. Shona followed him.

The Solway chart was pinned above the radio and the computer that ran the shout-management software. He checked the tide tables and pressed his lips together.

'If we were searching for a missing tender, one that had run oot of fuel or suffered an engine failure, we'd start here.' He drew a triangle radiating out from the stone pier at Hildan Island, then caught her expression and sighed. 'You want me to have a wee look, don't you?'

'Tommy, I'd really appreciate it. Put the word out, see if anyone's heard anything.'

'I'm not hearing much these days,' he replied and stomped back to his tea and paperwork.

'Why's that?' Shona teased. 'Not friends with the police anymore?'

He grinned, but there was something edgy in his expression and the smile faded quickly. Perhaps, despite the money the film-makers were paying him, his troubles were financial. Might also be why he'd taken on the *Ramsey Ranger*'s repairs. Shona was about to ask how things were generally, but Tommy appeared absorbed in his work.

'Okay. Let me know,' she said, getting up.

'Aye. I will,' he said, not looking up.

-

When Shona returned to High Pines, she sat on the sofa in the lounge with Becca, accompanied by a couple of pizzas from the freezer, a bottle of soft drink and a movie playing on the TV that neither of them really watched.

For the first time in a while, Shona felt herself relax. She sensed that Becca was also reassured by the presence of their guests. Just having Ben and Ric close by, whose sole purpose was to keep others safe, was reassuring. But if their fortress was not to become a prison, Shona needed to find whoever was targeting McGowan. Equally pressing was the threat posed by Delfont to her family. She'd need to neutralise that alone. As her mind drifted from the film, she felt the familiar sensation of cogs turning over.

'It's okay if you want to do some work.' Becca yawned, having felt her mother shift and fidget beside her. 'I might go to bed in a minute.'

Shona got up and stretched, her ribs hardly protesting at all. 'I'll just look at a few things and then I'll get some sleep myself,' she assured her daughter and crossed to the table by the window, where her files were piled in boxes. A minute later, Becca drifted out, calling goodnight. When she had gone downstairs, Shona opened her laptop.

Now Shona could think of Delfont and the money laundering as an investigation, she found she could distance herself, view the evidence dispassionately, almost like scenes from a movie. She opened a folder and began to read the papers inside.

The case against Rob rested on the existence of transactions signed off by him, making him a *money mule*: an unwitting participant in the process to integrate illegal funds into legal businesses. Rob's lists regularly contained hundreds of entries he was supposed to check. Fraud was an issue, but most of this supervision was to ensure no employee was losing the bank's money through poor practice, excessive risk or incompetence. If profits were going up, a team didn't face much scrutiny. She knew of a case where an employee raised an alarm on a similar laundering account – a small garage operation that went from £30K to £4 million in a matter of weeks – only for the bank to take a further eighteen months to freeze the transactions.

Part of her was scared that she was wasting her time by burying herself in the minutiae of figures and five-year-old banking transactions. But instinct told her that if she didn't look here, she would always wonder if what she needed had been right under her nose and she'd missed it.

Her mind drifted back to her guests, and some of the scenes she'd witnessed them filming. What did Robert Burns, the exciseman, have to teach Shona Oliver, police officer? Goods and cash had always moved across borders. One thing hadn't changed: follow the money. She knew where the laundered funds had gone – into gold and out of the country. But where had the money come from? If she could trace the origins, flow and whereabouts of illicit income, then illegally acquired assets could be frozen or confiscated, and those who had committed the original offences and the subsequent laundering might be apprehended. The place to start was not among the banking records but with Delfont's financial profile. He had to have hidden his gains somewhere.

She looked at the clock. It was after ten o'clock, but not too late to call Thalia Brookes. Maybe she didn't have to do this alone.

'How are you?' Shona asked.

There was a long pause. 'I'm okay.' Thalia sounded far from okay, and the slurred edge to her words made Shona wonder if she'd been drinking or taking prescription meds.

Shona swallowed, aware that what she was going to say to Thalia might not have the effect she hoped for.

'We're both experienced and intelligent police officers. What d'you think Delfont is going to do now?'

'Move on. Find other victims,' Thalia said flatly.

'I agree, and I'm not prepared to let him do that. It's why I'm asking for your help.' Shona took a deep breath. If this was going to work, she would have to share everything with Thalia. 'I think Delfont was behind the money laundering. He's why Rob was jailed on false charges. I believe he and the criminal gang he's associated with targeted both of us, believing that Rob wouldn't reveal his dodgy pay-off from the bank and I wouldn't report what happened while I was apparently driving my car under the influence. We both had so much to lose. Delfont gambled we'd never reveal these things, even to each other.'

'Clever, you've got to admit,' Thalia said, without enthusiasm.

'How many female officers d'you know who didn't report a sexual assault?' Shona went on. 'I never thought I'd be one of them. I fell into the trap of thinking that 'cos I was a cop, I was too clever. I'd never get cornered on my own. In a straight fight Delfont might have won, but I'd have made the bastard sorry, and he knew that too. It's why he drugged us.'

Thalia grunted in agreement. 'Coward, ain't he?'

'By threatening both Rob and me, he made sure neither of us was in a position to come after him, or be taken seriously. Now even the CPS think I'm a liar covering for my corrupt husband.'

Shona felt the reignited anger building. She'd meant to lay out a reasoned case to Thalia, a considered line of enquiry that would give her former colleague hope that all avenues hadn't been explored and out there, somewhere, was a way to nail Delfont, but now she just felt barely controlled rage.

'And it's not over, Thalia. He put my husband in jail, and now he's threatening me and my daughter if Rob appeals. Yeah, I want revenge, but more than that I want justice. We need to take the fight to Delfont. I want him stripped of his assets, his credibility, his reputation, and I want him put away for a long, long time.'

Shona realised she was shaking. She'd never expressed what she wanted so clearly, even to her therapist, but she knew Thalia was perhaps the only one who would truly understand.

'I've been thinking the same,' Thalia said, sounding a fraction more like her old self.

Shona remembered the discussion earlier with Vanda about serial killers. Investigations into such cases often began with connections to a suspect's job, home and social circle. Work, rest and play, as it was dubbed – a riff on the old Mars bars slogan. She repeated it to Thalia, who murmured her agreement.

'Operation Vita would've looked for Delfont's criminal financial connections,' Shona began, thinking of the maze of shell companies, offshore accounts and money transmitters that hid financial trails. 'We don't have the resources to go over that again.'

'And *work* is a problem,' Thalia said. 'Gonna get us nowhere talking to colleagues. We can't know who's compromised by Delfont. That leaves *rest* and *play*. So home and social circle.'

'Let's start with the basics: house purchases,' Shona said. She knew Delfont was originally from Basildon in Essex, close to the coast and well connected to the City of London, a thirty-minute train journey away. It was a post-war new town whose population had mostly come from London's East End, with a five-foot high Hollywood-style sign on its approaches, and a poor-but-party-hard reputation.

'He's from the Craylands estate,' Thalia said. 'I've already been lookin' into his connections there. The place pops up regular as a hotspot for Essex Police. Most reported crime is of a violent or sexual nature, so he'd be right at home, he would. I can work on getting addresses. Kick over a couple o' rocks and see what vermin crawls out.'

Shona googled the area. The top hits were all crime stories about this 'troubled estate', and included an image of local market stall displaying replica guns and a baseball bat wrapped in barbed wire. 'Be careful,' she said, eyes on the screen. 'I'm not happy about you going in alone.'

'It's better that way. I'll just be another Black woman. Ain't nobody gonna take much notice of me.'

'Well, they'll take notice after we nail this bastard,' Shona said. 'Listen, can you hold off for a day? There's a woman who worked with Rob I need to see. I'm supposed to be meeting her tomorrow if I can get away.'

'You busy?'

'Don't you read the papers?' Shona said with mock indignation. 'Hang on.'

Shona sent her a link and heard Thalia's familiar cackle.

'Oh my days, I seen less dubious sights staggering out of Chinawhite's in the 90s,' Thalia said, referring to a notorious nightclub in London's Piccadilly that had been popular with celebrities.

'It's been mentioned,' Shona said. As probationary PCs they'd both completed secondments as beat cops with the neighbouring Met, which included clearing post-clubbing debris, human or otherwise, from London's West End. She was glad to hear Thalia laugh. 'Best of it is, I've now got the celebrity in question installed in my basement, with his bodyguards, till he finishes filming.'

'That sounds a little too dominatrix for my liking. What kind of establishment you running there, sassy girl?'

It was Shona's turn to smile. 'We had some good times working together, didn't we?'

Shona's therapist had once told her that a useful exercise to help moderate some common symptoms of PTSD – including blinding rages and hyper-vigilance – was to reinforce other, positive, memories from the same time period. So she chatted to Thalia about the rewarding jobs – lives saved or turned around, the camaraderie of the good colleagues who had your back on the toughest shouts – to balance out the darkness they both carried.

'I'll be glad when this film job is over, seriously,' Shona said, her thoughts returning to the present. 'Don't think babysitting famous folk is my forte.' Then, seeing the walkie-talkie on the table and the boxes of files around her, she said, 'I'll be happier when both these jobs are over. But one thing's for certain.'

'What's that?' Thalia asked.

'I'm pleased you're with me on this,' Shona said, and meant it.

'Me too, mate. Me too.'

Chapter 22

Next morning, Shona didn't so much wake up as realise she'd been awake for some time: eyes closed but brain turning over. The sense of taking action conjured by last night's discussion with Thalia had been replaced by a checklist of obstacles that loomed before her like a mountain of winding roads, steep drops and hairpin bends. But they'd tackle them, she and Thalia, one by one, until they arrived at the destination they both needed and deserved.

She picked up the walkie-talkie from beside her bed. Above her in the lounge, she could hear Becca moving about. She checked her phone. She'd slept long and deep. It was almost nine a.m. Shit.

She came into the lounge in jeans, a T-shirt and bare feet, still towelling her hair dry from the shower. 'Becca, I've got to go out later, what are—'

She stopped. James McGowan was sitting by the window, cross-legged on the floor with his back to her. When he turned and smiled, she saw he had a screwdriver in his hand and was rewiring the broken plug on the floor lamp which had remained unrepaired since Rob's court case. McGowan's face still carried the red dye but the bandages on his hands had been replaced by thinner, less restrictive, individual dressings.

'Morning,' he said. 'Y'know, when I first went tae London I worked as a painter and decorator. I really wanted to be an electrician, but I had tae give it up for the acting.'

'Isn't it supposed to be the other way around? People give up acting for other jobs.' She thought that this might be the moment to bring up their past association. How she remembered that he'd talked about both acting and the more realistic ambition of being an electrician, at school. But she felt irritated by the way he appeared to have made himself at home in her lounge without even acknowledging how she might feel. She stopped short of immediately booting him back down to the guest suites, wrong-footed by this new McGowan with his easy chat and apparently helpful DIY. She settled the towel around her neck and eyed him suspiciously.

'Oh, I wanted to be an actor awright, but I dinnae see one job as being better than the other. Becca's outside wi' security, by the way.' He indicated with his screwdriver, and Shona went to the floor-to-ceiling bay window and looked down. Becca seemed to be taking turns with Ric and Ben to run up the steep garden steps while being timed. By the look of delight on her face, she was beating them.

'I had ma house in the US rewired recently and the guys let me tag along.'

Probably star-struck, Shona thought.

'I learned a lot from them,' he went on. 'You should get this place done.' He swept his screwdriver around the lounge. 'Recessed spots are a bit dated.'

Shona thought of their debts. Just getting from one day to the next was all she could manage. McGowan must have read something in her expression.

'Doesnae need to be done now. I can sketch you a plan.'

'Thanks,' said Shona.

He looked up at her, one eye closed against the sun that streamed in. 'You think I don't remember you, don't you? Clocked ye the minute you walked on the set. Wee Shona Mackenzie.'

Shona stared at him, stunned by the ease with which he'd maintained a front.

'You knew it was me,' Shona said, indignant. 'Why'd you no' say something?' She suddenly felt foolish, as if he'd hoodwinked her, but then she hadn't said anything either.

'Wasnae sure you'd remember me.' He gave her a shy smile. 'Bit embarrassed, I suppose. Look what you've done wi' your life. Catching bad guys for real, not just in the movies. All the wrongs you make right. I'm just muckin' about. Also, you're pretty intimidating, especially when you're pissed off.'

'So, don't piss me off,' Shona said, arms folded in a stance every member of Dumfries CID would recognise as the final pre-suspension, out-on-your ear, warning. But her expression had softened.

'Fair point,' James conceded, ruefully, giving the plug he was holding a final turn with the screwdriver. He cocked his head, listening, as if to check the others were still outside. 'Last school disco, just before I left,' he said quietly, watching her from the corner of his eye. 'Still remember yon kiss.'

Shona felt the blush creeping up her neck to her cheeks. So he hadn't forgotten either. Another time, another place. She rubbed her hair with the towel again, giving herself a moment to recover her balance. Thoughts of James McGowan had been filed strictly away under *the past*, a place she rarely cared to visit. Now, memories flooded back: disco lights from the high gym hall windows colouring the playground puddles. His soft breath on her cheek, a single kiss from the guy she'd secretly fancied all year. Then he was gone.

'*Ae fond kiss, and then we sever*, eh?' McGowan said, quoting one of Burns's most famous love songs. 'Come a long way fae Garthamlock, both of us,' he said, gazing out of the window. As he did so, it struck Shona that this boy in the year above her, whom half the kids thought brilliant, and the other half a show-off arsehole, had in fact been a turning point in her life: him leaving for London had made her think she could do it too, that she could get out and have a better life. She glanced at the table and, among the boxes of Rob's paperwork, saw that the long-stemmed roses had migrated from their spot in the utility room, and she felt herself blush again.

James raised his chin towards the flowers, an amused look on his face.

'Not impressed, eh? I might have known you wouldnae be. Becca brought them up from the utility room,' he said. 'I asked her if there wis any jobs I could do, and she said aboot the light and showed me where the toolbox was. Dinnae be embarrassed. I'm the one who should be embarrassed kickin' aff like that. I'm such a dick.'

'Aye, you are,' Shona said, recovering herself and amused at his apparently genuine assessment of his own behaviour.

'I know, and I'm so, so sorry. Look, can we just rewind? Start again?' When she nodded, he continued, 'Hello, I'm James. Forgive me if I don't shake,' he said, holding up his hands still dotted with adhesive dressings.

'I'm Shona.' She smiled, suddenly feeling like an awkward teenager again. But perhaps this brush with the past wouldn't be so bad after all.

'I'm no' making excuses, but I forget I'm not this skinny, five-foot-seven wean anymore. That's average height for a Glasgow man, by the way,' he said, flashing another smile. 'I forget that people dinnae realise I'm still Jazza-fae-the-Scheme. They see all the millions the studios make, those big-grossing films, and somehow transfer that to me. But that's not me. Never was, never will be. It's why I can't work out why somebody would hate me this much.' He held up his hands again to emphasise the point.

'Might not be hate, might be love,' Shona said, thinking about what the therapist had told her.

'Aye,' he replied, his expression serious. 'That's an even scarier thought.'

Shona established that James — he was no longer just *McGowan* to her — and his security staff planned to stay at High Pines all day. Barry the scriptwriter and director Simon Jones were coming over to discuss their next move. Becca could get on with her studies. Shona impressed upon her the need for secrecy over James's location and that Becca shouldn't go off anywhere without either Ben or Ric.

The weather had turned cold again, after its earlier promise, and rain had swept in from the west. The forecast for the day was stormy. Becca was happy enough to stay home with her new friends, who'd promised to talk to her later about surviving in desert environments. 'Be good for my archaeology training,' Becca had told her mother. 'Like my very own episode of *SAS: Who Dares Wins* off the telly.'

It better not be, Shona thought.

Shona set off in the Audi as soon as she'd had breakfast. Right up until the last moment she wondered if it was a good idea to meet Katherine 'Kanga' Jones, Rob's former colleague.

Anoushka had checked her out and assured Shona that she was who she said she was, but one sniff that this meeting had been prompted by a journalist and Shona would be out of there.

Shona hadn't the time to go to London, and Katherine didn't want to come up to Dumfries, so they'd agreed on a compromise. The Australian had family business in Manchester and agreed to meet at the Northbound Tebay Services on the M6, a ninety-minute drive for both. The barrister had offered to come up, but Shona didn't think it would be necessary. She'd have a good idea if what the woman had to say was useful.

When she crossed the border into Cumbria, Shona's phone rang. She pulled into the inside lane and answered it. Professor Kitchen, with the toxicology results for Michael Vincent.

'Benzos cocktail,' she said. 'Xanax's side effects include dizziness and trouble sleeping. Temazepam is used to treat insomnia, but its hypnotic side effects include dizziness, euphoria, motor and cognitive impairment. Taking one doesn't cancel the effects of the other out like some people think. This is pointing more and more to accident or suicide.'

Shona couldn't argue with that, so she didn't.

'Look, what you said to me the other day about Rob… you were right.'

'I'm glad to hear it,' Slasher Sue replied. 'I'll be even more glad when you're out of danger.'

'It's in hand,' Shona replied.

'Good. Let me know if I can help. I don't like my friends ending up on my table, except in restaurants.' And with that cheery thought, she hung up.

Charming. You can take a joke too far, Shona thought as she moved out to overtake a caravan. But it was a timely reminder just how high the stakes were.

The road passed Carlisle and began to climb out of the peat bogs and saltmarshes of the Solway Mosses towards the rolling Cumbrian hills. Far to her right, Shona glimpsed the snow-laden peaks of the Lake District, before the next veil of cloud swept in.

Ten minutes later, her phone buzzed again. This time it was Kate.

'Any sign of that *U will dye* note yet, Kate?' Shona said.

'Not yet, boss, but forensics are back on the IED. Ammonium nitrate and fuel oil similar to the composition used in the Oklahoma City Bombing, but obviously a fraction of the size.'

'What's the possible origin of material like that?'

'You can buy it as a pure chemical or collect it from some fertilisers and some instant cold packs. It's also used in commercial explosives for mining and blasting. But there is some good news.'

'I'd really like to hear that.'

'It might be possible to recover latent fingerprints and DNA from the device, but it'll take a couple of days.'

'Okay, good,' Shona said, turning over the possibilities. 'Let's hope whoever did this is on our system. Anything else?'

'We're seeing attempts to trend James McGowan on social media,' Kate replied. 'We've been trying to ID suspects, but it's like a tidal wave. Multiple negative allegations. I've got Vinny on it, but the sources seem to be fake accounts on Twitter, Instagram and Facebook – difficult to establish if they're local. His agent in the US and his lawyers are getting the users blocked, but it's whack-a-mole.'

'Nasty?'

'Very. Paedophile allegations. Stories he's a wife-beater. Deepfake photos of him partying with a certain ex-president, but you can mostly spot those 'cos AI has trouble with hands for some reason, so Vinny tells me. Oh, and more environmental stuff.'

Fucksake. What makes these folk tick? she thought.

'Any indication this is the Arctic Guardians?' Shona said, prepared to review her earlier conclusion that the group weren't implicated in the attacks.

'Nothing. In fact, they've pointed out the claims he polluted a ranch in Montana with a banned pesticide as total rubbish on all levels. The attacks are just everything you can think of. A real demolition job. There's lots of upset people on his fan sites and chatrooms.'

James hadn't said anything. She knew he didn't run his own accounts, and she had the distinct impression that his management team kept the day-to-day grime away from him, but all the same, it was a bit too much of a coincidence that this had happened now. She was fairly sure the same individual who was behind the online attacks had also planted the IED and, possibly, caused Michael Vincent's death. It had the feeling of an orchestrated campaign, and the web was another way to move around unseen. You just had to wind folk up and watch them go. James's people could issue denials, lawyer's injunctions, take down sites and block users, but somewhere in some dusty corner of the internet, a trace would always remain.

She was daily and profoundly thankful that Delfont's video of her assault hadn't made it online.

'Okay, Kate. Thanks. Let me know if Vinny or forensics come up with anything.'

For the rest of the drive, Shona sat in silence as the intermittent rain turned to steady sleet. The attacks on James seemed so personal, she couldn't see how they could come from a stranger. Why would you invest the time, money and energy, and risk a prison sentence, for someone you'd never met? But perhaps this individual didn't consider themselves a stranger. They'd been so deeply wounded by James that even a quick death wasn't enough. They wanted to draw it out, destroy him so completely that no one would ever mention his name without associating it with foul deeds.

She pulled off the M6 at Tebay Southbound Services, and looped back along the un-signposted service road to the northbound carpark. She switched off her engine and sat, thinking about her anger at Delfont. What would compel her to conduct a campaign like this against him? Becca had been targeted once before by a criminal who thought he could get to Shona by threatening her daughter. She'd defend her again, to the death, but that was different from taking the law, with all its imperfections, into your own hands. If you usurped the law, you'd become the person you hated most. A piece of their evil would take root in you. Where was the victory in that?

On a winter weekday, the usual packs of tourists heading either for the Lake District or Scotland were absent. The sleet lay on the fields and fells, and the view of the small lake and stands of bare trees had become a timeless black-and-white photograph that some centuries-old winter shepherd would recognise.

Shona stamped her shoes free of the sleet as she entered the stone building. A woman in her thirties, generously wrapped in a pink puffer jacket, jeans and Ugg boots stood by the services' farm shop. Kanga was distinguishable by her glossy blonde hair and tan in the middle of British January pallor. Shona, normally good at remembering faces, stared at the woman whose gift had sat on her daughter's bed for years and struggled to recognise her.

'Katherine?' Shona said, offering her hand.

Kanga wanted an Americano, so Shona ordered two, which they took to a quiet table by the window. The woman seemed to shrink away from the winter landscape as it pressed up against the glass.

'Takes a bit of getting used to again,' she said. 'I'm here to sort out my grandmother's estate. Sell the house in Manchester.'

'I'm sorry,' Shona replied.

'It's fine. We weren't close,' Kanga replied with a shrug.

It was the sort of story someone might make up to evoke sympathy. Shona thought of Becca's stuffed toy. 'My daughter still has the koala you gave her for Christmas.'

'It was a kangaroo. For her birthday.' Kanga smiled. 'Wow, she's still got it?'

'Ah, that's right.' Shona smiled back, reasonably satisfied that Anoushka had been right, and this wasn't some journalist posing as an ex-colleague to get a story. 'So how long did you work with Rob?'

Kanga took a sip of her coffee. 'A few years. I was shocked when I heard what happened.'

'It's been difficult,' Shona conceded. 'Anoushka said you had evidence that might help an appeal?'

Kanga set down her cup and leaned back, shivering. Outside, on the lake, a pair of ducks flew in, skittering on the ice as if they hadn't expected the hard landing.

'I had to come, so I could look you in the eye and say I'm sorry,' Kanga began. 'I was a kid. I didn't know what I was doing. That's not an excuse, just a fact.'

Despite the warmth of the room, Shona caught something of the surrounding chill creeping up her back, and her heart began to pound with anticipation.

'You were involved with the laundering?' Shona said softly. 'I'd understand if you felt threatened or were coerced.'

Kanga slid a USB flash drive from her pocket and pushed it across the table to Shona. 'Look, I'm heading back to Australia tomorrow. This might help. I copied some files as insurance against unfair dismissal. It's time sheets. I think the guys who were convicted fixed their submissions for when Rob was out of the office.'

'Okay.' It wasn't the breakthrough she'd hoped, but it was something.

'I'm sorry,' Kanga said. 'It wasn't serious. I never expected Rob to leave you. I knew he never would, but I realise what I did was wrong. I'm not the sort of person who dates married men. I came here because I owe it to Rob, to you and to myself to help.'

Shona stared at her, re-running the woman's words inside her head until she knew there was no other explanation. Rob had had an affair. With Kanga.

It was obvious from Kanga's expression that she believed Shona already knew, and had expected a sisterly chat about freeing the man they'd both loved. The flash drive dug into Shona's flesh as she fought to keep control of the anger bubbling in her chest, choking her into silence.

When Shona didn't say anything, Kanga looked uncertainly at her, then stood up.

'I'd better get back. Call me if there's anything I can do.'

'Oh, I think you've done enough,' Shona said bitterly and turned her gaze to the frozen landscape and the bleak fells. When she looked back, Kanga was gone.

Shona sat until her coffee was as cold and bitter as the landscape beyond the window. She looked down at the slim gold band of her wedding ring, which suddenly seemed to have become red hot, burning into her flesh. She slid it down towards her knuckle and, when it wouldn't go any further, sucked at her finger. The ring tasted bitter and metallic, like blood, but came off. She shoved it into the zipped section of her purse. Then she picked herself up for the journey home. The sleet had turned to snow, and she was suddenly anxious she'd be caught in this place and fail to reach the safety of High Pines. But was it safe now? Every room, every view reminded her of him and this new, and ultimate, betrayal.

Chapter 23

Shona opened the curtains to a rare, bright stillness over the estuary. After the previous day's storm, the water was now a mirror reflecting the trees on the far bank. It was still early. The few boats not bundled away under awnings at the sailing club sat like contented mice on the open water, lulled by the winter sun and oblivious to the next storm that might pounce.

She heard a tap on her door and looked up. Becca came in with a mug of tea.

Her daughter had clearly known that something was amiss when her mother came home, white-faced, the previous evening. Shona wasn't about to enlighten Becca as to what she'd learned, but she felt guilty that her daughter was worrying, and had assured her it was nothing to do with the man threatening her father.

Becca had also noticed her mother's missing wedding band, but Shona had told her that it simply needed tightening, and she hadn't wanted to lose it. There was always a danger on the lifeboat that, in hauling a casualty from the sea, a ring might slip off. Shona often left her expensive 18ct gold ring, made in London by the royal jewellers Garrard, at home or locked with the valuables at the station when out on shouts, but Becca had taken it as further proof that her mother must be losing weight from worry and overwork.

Now, although she'd hardly slept, Shona smiled brightly and declared she'd just been tired, but felt better.

'Good, 'cos the boys want to know if you'll take them for a run,' Becca said. 'I told them that you usually go out to Knockie Point, but hadn't been for a while.'

She really didn't want to face James and the security team, but at the sight of Becca's anxious face, she agreed. She'd be down in ten minutes. Who knew? The run might do her some good.

They set off along the coastal path, with Shona and James running side by side in the lead, setting the pace, and Ric and Ben close behind. Shona nodded to a couple of dog walkers they passed, but otherwise the track was quiet. She still had the same sensation she'd had on the island, of being watched. *Hyper-vigilance* was what Sue Kitchen had called it, and Shona thought she had every reason to be. She scanned the trees as they entered the wooded section of the path, then reminded herself that despite her local knowledge, Ric and Ben were the experts here and would peg any threat before she did.

They were soon in a steady rhythm and Shona found that, although her muscles protested and her heart rate was higher than normal, she felt exhilarated at being able to put her troubles to one side, if only for a little while.

When they reached the point, she slowed and the men stopped to admire the curve of the small bay, thickly banked with white cockle shells down to the smooth water that reflected the deep blue of the winter sky. Ben and Ric walked a little further on, and began a programme of stretches and lunges while still keeping an eye on their charges.

'You've probably seen the stuff on the web about me,' James said as he eased out his hamstrings. 'I didn't beat my wife.'

'My team are already on it. I'm sorry. I can't imagine how difficult it must be,' she said with feeling. The longevity of the internet meant this was unlikely to be the last time he'd find it necessary to issue a denial. 'I think it's the same individual from the Burns Supper attack that's targeting you. We'll catch whoever's doing it.'

James gave her a small smile of thanks, and she returned it.

'It's a nice place you've got,' he said. 'Just you and your daughter running it? Lilly said your husband was in prison.'

Shona's smile tightened.

'Money laundering,' she said lightly. 'He didn't do it. He's going to appeal.'

That was enough. Don't elaborate. Don't explain. Don't say Rob Oliver is a lying, duplicitous, PA-shagging bastard as well.

Given yesterday's jaunt with James down memory lane to their shared roots in Garthamlock, one of the roughest schemes in the city, she thought he might make some crack about associating with a better class of criminals now, but he just nodded.

'Must keep you busy.' He put out a hand to indicate she should lead the way down across the shingle to the water's edge. Shona was glad of the moment away from prying eyes to swallow the mix of anger, grief and panic that had been threatening to engulf her since the meeting with Kanga. She was sure it had welled up enough to be visible in her expression.

'It's lovely here, int it?' he said. 'Lilly was right. Ideal spot for a business like yours.'

A business that may not last much longer, Shona thought.

'What's happening with the filming?' she asked, keen to change the subject.

'Shooting some stuff later.'

'What about the dye? Isn't that a problem?' She looked at him closely for the first time, then checked her own hands. The colour on his face did seem to have lessened in a way it hadn't on her own skin.

'Looks better, doesn't it?' James grinned.

Shona nodded. In the small pits and lines of his remarkably healthy-looking skin, traces of the dye were just visible, but it was much better than she expected.

'The make-up lasses came yesterday when you were oot and gave me a facial. Full exfoliation,' he said.

'Really,' Shona said, suppressing a grin that had crept up on her despite her low mood.

'Make-up will cover the rest. I can get back to work now.' He caught her expression and narrowed his eyes. 'What?'

She shook her head. 'What would the young Jazza think about that? You'll be having a manicure next.'

'I like a manicure. A pedicure too.' He wedged one foot behind the other, then flipped off his expensive trainer like a football move, catching it deftly in one hand. He wiggled rainbow-painted toes in front of her. 'I'm secure in my masculinity. Actually, my kids love it. They think it's cool.'

Shona let the smile take hold. 'What would the young Jazza say to you now?'

'I think he'd say what he always said. Be who you are.' He slipped his trainer back on. 'What about you? What would the young Shona say to you?'

Shona thought for a moment but couldn't answer.

He must have seen her expression and shook his head. 'You haven't changed,' he said. 'You're the same girl you always were. Just… more. You've grown into yerself. You were always smart, funny and resourceful. Beautiful.' He paused, reached up and took a curl of her hair, letting it run through his fingers. She stepped back from him, confused, and he held up a palm in apology. 'Sorry. Just sayin'.' He took a breath. 'You and I are alike,' he went on. 'Your work matters to you, but it's no' just turning up and knowing your lines, is it? Gotta do the very best job you can do. Maybe it's aboot where we're both from. We'd a chance through luck or fate or whatever you wannae call it, and we've seized life with both hands because we know what happens if you let your chance slip by. There's nae network to cushion the bumps. Nae houses, nae money to soften the blow while you recover yerself. It's like standing up in the surf. Once you lose yer footing, you plummit.'

She saw the truth in his words. It was something Rob could never understand.

He smiled his old, self-deprecating smile. Jazza the clown. Jazza the chancer.

'People normally think I'm off ma heid, when I say things like that.'

'No, it's not crazy,' Shona replied. 'I know exactly what you mean.

—

The outdoor set for the storming of the smuggler ship *Rosamond* was down a rutted lane to a creek on a private estate, not far from where the real vessel had run aground and been overcome by customs officers, dragoons and Robert Burns. One quarter of the hull had been created from wood, and the rest would appear in post-production CGI. With the absence of Michael Vincent as Burns's friend John Syme, the scene had been hastily rewritten to replace the action in which he would have featured.

James McGowan had become Burns once more, striding among the red-coated soldiers, heat and light rippling from him. He looked invincible, but Shona knew different.

Matt and the other security guards had been taken in hand by Ric and Ben, who harried them into position on the perimeter of the set, a good cop, bad cop duo that praised effort, ridiculed the uncommitted, and demanded one hundred per cent from everyone. They insisted McGowan returned to their fourbie between takes, which to Shona's surprise he did. She glimpsed him through the passenger window, leafing through his Burns book, deep in thought.

Shona checked the shoreline. The tide was out. Anyone approaching would need to cross the mud flats, risking a literal sticky end. As she walked alone through the dead bracken, rusted to the colour of old blood, a hare ran out into the path and halted, stock-still, in front of her. They were no more than a few metres apart. Shona paused, determined not to frighten it, but the hare didn't move. Shona took a step forward, but it remained frozen. She took another step. It was only when she was almost close enough to touch it that it darted away through an arch of bracken. As she passed the spot, Shona saw, in the corner of her vision, that the creature hadn't disappeared. Instead, the gimlet stare of the hare's dark eye looked back at her from between the fronds. Shona shivered. The day had a raw dampness that seemed to claw at her through the layers of wool and waterproof. A scent, bitter and rank, was coming from somewhere close on the marsh.

Murdo had once told her about the witches of Burns's poem 'Tam o' Shanter', and how folklore in Dumfries and Galloway had it that those resourceful women possessed the ability to turn themselves into hares in order to move around undetected and perform their malign deeds. But Shona had the uncomfortable sense that what she'd witnessed was not the manifestation of mischief, but a warning of a greater evil yet to show itself.

—

When she got back to High Pines that evening, she found that Ric and Ben had arranged with Becca that they'd cook a vegetarian risotto for everyone. Becca had spent some of her day at the pub with Freya and Tommy, and had chopped the mushrooms and onions in preparation. Shona didn't mind. In fact, she was touched by the way everyone seemed to be rallying round to help.

After the adrenaline high that must have come during the fight scene, James was quiet through dinner, which they ate at the kitchen table. When they'd finished, and the washing-up was done, she left Becca with the three men, playing a card game that looked suspiciously like poker, to go upstairs to the lounge. She was expecting a call from Rob and needed to prepare herself on every level.

She'd looked at the files on Kanga's flash drive. The woman was thorough, if nothing else, and it crossed Shona's mind that she'd make an efficient blackmailer.

Kanga and Rob left the office early roughly twice a week – nights that corresponded to Shona's regular late shifts, when Becca's babysitter had normally come in. This pattern had gone on for eighteen months. *Eighteen months.* Not a quick fling at a conference. Not a six-week infatuation, but a year and a half, through two Christmases, birthdays, anniversaries.

She'd believed there was someone once before. The year after Becca was born and Shona had hit rock-bottom with post-natal depression. Rob had denied any affair, and she'd convinced herself she was seeing shadows everywhere. She had believed she deserved to be abandoned. But slowly, with Rob's support, her life had turned around. Had her gratitude to him for turning a bleak future into a promise of sunshine blinded her to everything else? The contents of Kanga's flash drive were proof it might have done.

Shona struggled to concentrate on the tables and figures. Kanga had circled the names of the two fraudsters who'd already been charged, but also a third name – Ethan Brown, an intern who'd worked on the team for a three-month period at the time the co-mingling of legal and illegal transactions first began. She was just reading through the other documents on the drive when her phone rang.

'Hey, darlin'. How are you?' Rob sounded weary, tense.

Shona slammed the laptop shut and the documents disappeared. But she couldn't rid herself of the seething rage so easily.

'Still in the hospital?' Shona said, battling to keep her temper under control.

'Back on the wing. It's okay, though,' he said. 'Everything's cool.'

She considered telling him again that he must accept segregation but knew it was pointless. Perhaps, when he was truly scared, he'd change his mind and, if he was lucky, it wouldn't be too late. Given what she'd learned about his affair, she was having a hard time feeling any sympathy.

'Listen, I've been sent some material which might aid your appeal,' she began.

'I thought we said. Let that go for now.'

'It's from Katherine Jones,' she said, evenly, alert for his reaction to her name.

There was a pause. She heard him swallow. Shona closed her eyes. It told her everything she needed to know. Great granite blocks of her life were shifting. The person she'd become since she'd left the poverty, the violence and the fear of her early life now seemed to be crumbling. James thought she hadn't changed, but she had. She'd covered over the skin of an abandoned child, and now the fake apparel she'd worn since then had melted away, and she was red raw and bare. But she wouldn't let Rob see it. She wouldn't let him know what he'd done to her.

She fought to keep her voice steady, because this wasn't just about Rob and the mess he'd created. It was about Becca. And her safety came before anything else.

'Kanga gave me a name. Ethan Brown.'

'Who?' Rob said, sounding genuinely puzzled.

'Intern. Joined you just as the laundering started.'

'What did he look like?'

'I don't have a picture.'

'Look, just stop, Shona. At least till things calm down.'

She could hear the fear in his voice. They'd been married for eighteen years. She didn't have to say out loud that she knew about his affair with Kanga. The mention of the woman's name and Shona's tone would've been enough. He might be locked up in a prison full of murderers, but now that wasn't the only thing he had to worry about, and she was glad he'd have time on his hands to think over how great his transgression had been.

'Can I talk to Becca? My credit's nearly gone.'

It certainly is, thought Shona.

'She's downstairs playing cards with some friends. Is there time for me to get her?'

'Don't think so. Tell her I love her, and I'll see her soon.'

Another lie.

'Okay,' Shona said. There was no reason their daughter should suffer and, for all Rob had done, Becca was the apple of his eye. 'Be careful...' she said, but the line had dropped and all there was between them was dead air.

Shona paced the room. She went to the window and saw the pine trees swaying in the increasing wind, dark masses against a darker sky. The brief lull of good weather was over. Another storm was on its way.

She couldn't face calling Thalia, although she had promised she would. Instead, she opened a text and sent the name Kanga had given her, Ethan Brown.

Thalia's reply came back immediately. *ACK. APE BF. ED. X*

Acknowledged. All Points East Brought Forward. It meant Thalia had already been to Basildon. *Expect Delivery.* And she'd found something. What? If she was ready to share it, she would have. For now, Shona would have to wait.

Chapter 24

It was a day for funerals. A sea fog had rolled in overnight, flattening the light and playing tricks with perspective. Nothing was where it should be. As Shona drove to the crematorium on the outskirts of Dumfries, she noticed the ungrazed grass in the fields, the absent geese. Their hedgerow cousins had fallen silent, and the world with them. No birdsong, no breeze stirred the grey air.

The High Pines guests had departed early that morning. A drive to Glasgow and then a shuttle flight to London for Michael Vincent's funeral. James had offered her a seat on the plane, but she had other goodbyes to make.

The CID team – Murdo, Kate, Ravi and DI Dalrymple – waited inside an arched timber building designed to resemble a Viking longhouse, which served as the reception area for mourners. They were dressed in sombre black, and stood apart from Sean and Taylor Nicolson's family and friends. Shona shook hands with Dalrymple and murmured greetings to the others.

The cortege arrived. Sean Nicolson's coffin was shouldered, and Taylor's small white casket led the funeral party into the chapel, as befitting a family man who always put his daughter first. Sonya Nicolson looked pale and even thinner than when Shona had last seen her in the corridor of the hospital. Baby Noah was carried by a woman who resembled Sonya so closely that she could only be the sister from Aberdeen.

After the ceremony, Shona moved along the family line, shaking hands and expressing sympathy for their loss. A fund had been created to help Sonya and Noah, who'd been left with little, to begin to rebuild, and there'd been a collection from the police and CID office to add to it. Sonya held tight to Shona's hand, thanking her.

'Sean didn't know it was a fake iPad,' Sonya said.

'I'm sure he didn't,' Shona replied, squeezing the woman's cold fingers. She wished she could offer her the consolation that those who'd sold her husband the knock-off tablet had been caught, understood the gravity of her loss, and showed appropriate remorse, but no arrests had yet been made. 'Sean couldn't have known what would happen. No one can see the future, and no one can change the past. We just have to deal with the now.' It sounded trite, even to her own ears, but Sonya nodded, apparently comforted by the sentiment.

DI Dalrymple was working the room, talking to as many people as he could, reassuring them that every avenue was being pursued. In his position Shona would be doing the same, but this wasn't her case and she felt like an interloper. Ravi and Kate were following in his wake, so Shona moved away to join Murdo.

'Any news?'

'Joe Dylan, Taylor's birth father, has been charged over the warehouse fire. Insurance job, like we thought. He was out on licence, so straight back inside. Wondered if he might request to attend today, but it's a blessing fur the family that he didnae.'

'What about the fake iPads?'

Murdo's face was sombre as he shook his head. 'Dan had some leads, but there's reports of counterfeit tablets overheating and catching fire in Wales and Dublin, as well as Cumbria. Looks like they're from the same batch. High value, small enough to be moved around. Smuggler's dream.' He lowered his voice. 'Think you'll be coming back soon?'

'Why, is there a problem?' Shona frowned.

'No, nae problem. But I think Dalrymple's anxious to get hame, and there's not much more he can do here. And thon filming must be near finished. It's a bad business, that stalker. Anyone who pulls a stunt like that at a Burns Supper deserves the book throwing at them, and I'm no' talkin' aboot the collected works of the bard.'

'McGowan always carries a copy of Burns's work with him. It's hefty. It'd do some damage.' Shona smiled.

'Does he now?' Murdo looked impressed. 'Well, let's hope forensics come up with something from that IED. As powerful a writer as Burns was, I think he'll be needing a wee bit help when it comes to redress.'

-

When Shona got home, she saw Tommy's van outside the lifeboat station and wondered if he had any news on the Zodiac missing from Hildan Island.

Becca was down in the garden studio, working on a homework project. James and his security team were due any minute, having flown straight back to Glasgow after Michael Vincent's funeral.

Shona jogged down the garden steps and put her head into the cabin.

'I'm just popping over to see Tommy,' Shona said. 'Lock the gate after me, and I'll come via the driveway, okay?'

'Okay,' Becca said. 'I'm just finishing this graph. Dinner is in an hour. Veggie lasagne.'

'I'll be back, don't worry. Call me if you need to.' Shona pulled the gate towards her, and waited until she heard Becca slide the bolt and turn the key.

At the RNLI station, she first checked that Tommy wasn't working on the lifeboat. The *Margaret Wilson* lay snug in her cradle; the boat hall was empty of shore crew, who often came in the evenings to do small maintenance jobs and chew the fat. She called Tommy's name as she went upstairs to the mezzanine level and heard an answering shout.

He was alone in the kitchen and lifted two cups down as she came in.

'Any luck with the Zodiac?' She pulled out a chair and sat down heavily. The run out to Knockie Point yesterday, followed by the traipsing across rough ground for the filming, was catching up with her.

'Nope. I wouldnae be surprised if someone's been off on their toes wi' that craft.'

'You know, the set security team, Matt and his crowd? They struck me as a bit fly.'

'Aye, it's probably insured so it'd be double payday for them.'

Shona nodded. They'd get nowhere proving anything if they couldn't trace the boat, which could be halfway to Norway by now. If it was Matt, or one of his team, they must be cursing their bad luck to have a sudden death on the same night they were spiriting away a boat, and then the police crawling all over the island. No wonder he looked shifty.

'Heard about thon funeral for the wee lassie on the news. Were you there?' Tommy said, his back to her, stirring the teas.

'I was.' Shona scrubbed her hands through her hair. 'Those things never get any easier. You just feel helpless. The mum kept telling me Taylor's father would never have bought the dodgy tablet if he'd realised. Trading Standards said previous iPad knock-offs were easy to spot, but now they're virtually identical to the real thing. Size, button placement, the Apple logo, they all look right. Sean Nicolson couldn't have known. If I was that wee girl's mother, that's what I'd want to believe.'

Tommy put the teas down and sat silent for a minute.

'Drink that up,' he said suddenly. 'I need a hand over at the *Ranger*. It'll no' take long.'

Shona checked the time. 'I've got half an hour.'

'That'll do,' Tommy replied.

–

They rowed across to the moored yacht in the dark, the oars catching ribbons of light from the lit windows of Kirkness. The hull and keel had miraculously escaped serious damage – probably due to the intervention of the *Margaret Wilson* – and just required minor patching. Most of the repairs were to the rudder, rudder shaft, rigging and electrics.

The main cabin was a mess of turned-out lockers and bundled-up sails. On the table sat the empty boxes of spare parts and chandlery that Tommy had already fitted.

'I'll have look at the bilge pumps,' Tommy said. 'Do a comms and navigation check for me, will ye?'

There was sufficient power in the boat's battery to get the radio going and Shona was soon on to Belfast Coastguard.

'Belfast Coastguard, Belfast Coastguard, this is yacht *Ramsey Ranger* requesting a comms and position check.'

'*Ramsey Ranger*, this is Belfast Coastguard, we're hearing you loud and clear. Please confirm your position.'

Shona reeled off the GPS co-ordinates.

'*Ramsey Ranger*, advise you check your AIS, not showing at that location.'

'Belfast Coastguard, this is *Ramsey Ranger*. Thank you for the update.'

Shona frowned. The Automatic Identification System was a piece of VHF-based navigation kit that helped prevent collisions by showing the identity and position of every vessel in the area. While it was only compulsory on vessels over fifteen metres, most boats carried them, partly to avoid being hit, but also to show their position in the event of an emergency – and the ten-metre *Ranger* obviously had one fitted.

Shona pulled out her phone and opened the marine traffic app, enlarging the map on the screen until there was no mistake. The location of the mooring buoy where the *Ramsey Ranger* lay showed another yacht tied up – the *Inspired*.

'What's going on, Tommy?' Shona said, suddenly aware he was standing in the cabin, one arm outstretched to lean on the overhead lockers.

'You'd better see this.'

He led her into the small forecabin, where the panels had been removed to accommodate fresh wiring.

'When I was a lad,' Tommy began slowly, 'I had a wee brush with smuggling. Videotapes. Music CDs. They cost a fortune in the mid-80s and a fella over on the Isle of Man asked if I'd bring them in fur him.' He ran a hand over his face. 'One time we had a rough passage and some of the boxes got wet. I opened one tae check on the contents and found cannabis. I wis just sixteen, but I knew it was trouble.'

'Did you report it?' Shona said.

'No, I didnae,' Tommy replied. 'But I stopped doing jobs for him. Wasnae easy. I'd only done it 'cos the boatyard was in trouble. My mother was tryin' to keep it going, but my faither was dead by then. I got a job wi' the oil. Worked up at Nigg an' that kept us afloat, just.'

Shona looked at the hull compartments and then Tommy, with a dawning understanding.

'And when we were called to rescue the *Ranger*, Larry Smith recognised you from back then?'

'Aye, he did. Dinnae know that's his real name. I knew him as Budger. He said if I didn't help fix the boat, he'd tell everyone I used tae run drugs. Paid me upfront, for repairs like. Said it was better if I just did the job and he went on his way.' Tommy shook his head. 'I wasnae that worried, but it'll scupper things wi' Freya. She wis married to an oil worker fae Shetland who went to prison for dealing on the rigs. There's no way she'd stay if she knew.'

'It was a long time ago,' Shona said. 'You were a kid, surely she'd see that?'

'Mibbaes,' Tommy said. 'But no guarantee.'

Shona thought back to the rescue and the way Larry Smith had kept her out of the cabin, even in the teeth of a gale, and she suddenly realised the reason for Tommy's anguish.

'You think the *Ranger* has something to do with the fake iPads?'

'Easy enough to swap your AIS unit with another boat.'

Shona opened the marine traffic app again and typed in the *Ramsey Ranger*. She turned the screen to show Tommy the boat's location, snug and safe in harbour at Douglas, on the Isle of Man.

Shona let out a long breath. 'Have you seen any iPads where they shouldn't be?'

Tommy shook his head. 'But the night after we brought the vessel in, a white van came and took stuff ashore. I told mysel' it was just personal kit, valuables he didnae want to leave, but...' He looked drained and Shona wondered at the toll Taylor Nicolson's death had taken on him, even though he wasn't to blame for any of it. And it hurt to think he hadn't been able to confide in her earlier.

'When was the last time you saw Larry Smith?' Shona asked.

'Days back. I've no contact for him but he said he'd be o'er to get the yacht.'

She remembered Murdo's words earlier. A *smuggler's dream* he'd called the counterfeit iPads. Small item, high value and easily sold on to unsuspecting folk in the run-up to Christmas. Now it looked like another shipment had arrived. There was CCTV at the petrol station on the main road. If the smugglers had been smart, they'd have stuck to back roads after that, but it was still possible they could pull an index number from the images.

'Let's keep this between us for now,' Shona said. 'Carry on with the repairs, but don't hurry. If Smith makes an appearance, call me.'

Chapter 25

Shona and Tommy rowed back to shore in near silence, each preoccupied by their own thoughts. Shona saw the headlights of the fourbie carrying James and his personal protection sweep up the hill and turn off for the gated High Pines parking area at the back of the house.

There was no doubt in Shona's mind that Tommy's remorse was genuine. He'd carried the guilt of his own wrongdoing and, through this attempt to make amends, she hoped he'd forgive himself. His motives as a lad supporting his widowed mother had been sound, even if his thinking had not.

As an eight-year-old, she'd been part of a shoplifting gang led by a Fagin-like teenage neighbour. She'd pocketed bags of marbles, sweets and small food items, and acted as a lookout while more valuable goods were spirited away. The reward had been protection from bullying. Once you were part of the gang, no one touched you.

But when a single tin of salmon had appeared in the pantry, when no such item could possibly have been purchased on their meagre household income, Shona's gran, Annie, became suspicious. A word was had with the ringleader's mother, and Shona found herself unemployed, and potentially a target for bullies once more. However, she was better able to stand up for herself by then, and it was generally held among the kids on the scheme that there'd be consequences for thumping the formidable Annie Mackenzie's wee granddaughter.

Shona had avoided punishment but she'd learned a valuable lesson in the complexities of right and wrong, and about the consequences of the choices you made. She often wondered if this had sparked the idea of joining the police. No one should condemn their past selves for the wrong choices made for the right reasons, no matter how late they found the chance to make amends. Perhaps it was Tommy's own brush with wrongdoing that had led him to give up so much of his time now to saving the lives of strangers in peril at sea.

Shona called Murdo to say she'd had a tip-off about the iPad smugglers and to check the CCTV from Kerr's garage and petrol station off the Kirkness road for a white van passing around midnight on the Sunday. She didn't mention the *Ramsey Ranger* at this stage. The link between the van and the iPads had to be established before the potential smuggling route could be extended, and a warrant to search and seize the yacht issued.

With the garden gate locked by Becca, Shona walked in the opposite direction from home, up the steep path that looped up behind the neighbouring properties and came out a little along the wooded cul-de-sac behind the house.

She ended the call as Murdo promised to update her.

When she came in sight of home, she stopped in her tracks. Outside High Pines was a noisy group, illuminated by the security lights. Most held up their phone cameras and were calling for James McGowan to come out. She also spotted the photographers who'd been at his hotel.

'What the…' Shona broke into a run, elbowing her way through the crowd as she dialled the house phone on her mobile. Ben answered.

'I'm outside. Let me in.'

The buzzer sounded. She pushed the gate.

'Get back,' Shona shouted as some of the fans tried to bundle themselves through after her. There was a flurry of flashes from the cameras. She gave the nearest fan a shove and slammed the gate behind her.

Ben was at the back door and turned the key as soon as she was inside.

'How did this happen?' Shona asked, knowing that it had always only been a matter of time before the fans and press realised that James was no longer at the hotel with the rest of the cast and crew.

'You better come in here,' Ben replied, his lean face serious as he led her through the utility room and into the kitchen.

Becca was at the table, sipping a glass of water. She looked tearful but defiant. Ric stood behind her, one hand on her shoulder. James was leaning against the sink, still in his dark suit and black tie, his arms folded. Ben carried on across the kitchen and disappeared down to the guest level.

'What is it?' Shona slid into a chair opposite Becca, her sense of dread mounting. She took her daughter's shaking hand.

'I was coming up the garden just now and he grabbed me,' Becca said. 'But I dug my heel in his shin and whacked him with my elbow, and ran up the steps before he could catch me.'

'Good girl.' Ric gave her shoulder a thumping pat of approval.

'Are you hurt?' Shona said, pushing back her daughter's dark hair with both hands and examining her face over and over in the bright illumination from the kitchen spot lights.

'I'm fine,' Becca said, but she looked shaken.

'Weapon?' Shona and Ric said, at the same moment.

Becca shook her head. 'Don't think so. He wanted to know where James was.'

Shona and Ric exchanged a glance. It was what they'd feared – the attacker would somehow follow up on the attempt he'd made on Burns Night – but they'd also planned for it and High Pines was as secure as they could make it.

'How d'you know it was a man?' Shona said.

'I didn't see him, but he was big and gruff, and he was speaking right in my ear. Couldn't tell where he was from, though. Didn't recognise the accent. Not London. Not here.'

'Can you remember his exact words, darling?' Shona said, taking her daughter's hand again and looking into her eyes, which were like a mirror of her own.

'He said, "What does he think he's up to? I know him. I know him." That was all, before I hit him.'

James McGowan looked shocked. 'This is ma fault. I've put you and Becca in danger.'

'It's the stalker's fault, mate. No one else's,' Ric replied firmly. 'It's possible he mistook Becca for you,' he said, directing the remark to Shona. 'Which means I want you both to be more careful.'

It was possible, Shona thought. She'd been in the studio earlier and, in the dark, apart from the difference in height, they looked similar. That he'd dared to come into the garden at High Pines felt like a violation.

Shona sat back and turned her phone over and over in her hand. Her first instinct was to haul in every single one of the fans and press outside, and grill them until someone remembered seeing something that could identify who'd laid hands on her daughter. The stalker had obviously used the cover of the fans and press, perhaps even arranged their arrival here with a tip-off on a fan site, but was likely long gone. Becca's description of a male, taller than she was, didn't match anyone Shona had seen in the group, who, apart from two photographers, appeared to be all women.

'And "what does he think he's up to" means what?' James said.

'Could be he's mad that you've moved accommodation, that you've taken steps to evade him,' Ric said. He'd obviously had experience of stalkers targeting other clients.

Shona thought back to what Vanda had said. 'It would certainly fit the profile the psychologist mentioned, a delusional intimacy seeker. "I know him. I know him." That's someone who believes they already have an intense relationship with you.'

But even as she said it, she knew there was another possibility. This was what she'd feared all along. Delfont's gang bringing threats right to her doorstep and turning the screw on Rob.

Before there could be any further discussion, Ben came back up the stairs, heavy torch and walkie-talkie in hand.

'Just had a mooch. We're under siege, top and bottom.'

'I'll get a patrol out to clear them,' Shona said. 'Apart from the inconvenience to us, I don't want paramedics directed away from calls 'cos some lassies are getting hypothermia and keeling over.'

'What about our prowler?' Ric said to Ben.

'The gate's still locked. Reckon he came over the fence. Looks like there's carpet fibres on some of the anti-climb spikes. Slung it over, left the same way, and took it with him. I asked the fans hanging about if they'd seen anything, but he must have got clear just before they arrived. Most are well put out that some nutter's stopping James popping out for a selfie. I think they would've said.'

'That fence is over two metres high,' Shona said. 'Whoever it was must have been fit.' The fibres might be something for forensics. Inside the fence was paving, and any footmarks in the grass outside had likely been obliterated by the fans.

Shona stood up and grabbed her phone. 'I'll call the patrol, and they can take Becca's statement.' She looked anxiously at her daughter. 'You okay with that?'

Becca nodded. Ric and Ben went to check on the fans and the press and advise them that the cops were on their way, and they should hop it.

James McGowan, who'd stood silent for most of the exchange, clapped his hands together. 'Right, cheese dreamies all round, I think.'

'What's that?' Becca said.

James looked at Shona, a grin on his face. 'Is that how you've brought your lassie up? Depriving her of gourmet food.' He turned back to Becca. 'It's a fried cheese and ketchup sandwich, hen. Have you no' had one?'

Becca shook her head, a smile forming on her lips.

He reached up for the heavy Le Creuset frying pan that hung near the hob. 'Recommended for shock, hangovers and heartbreak. Day we've had, we all deserve one. Right, may as well make myself useful. Where's your bread bin, darlin'?'

Shona watched from the door as she waited for the call to connect. Becca pointed to the cupboard, already distracted from her ordeal.

'It should really be a white pan loaf,' James went on. 'But I suppose wholemeal will have to do since we're posh. I make these for my kids. D'you wannae get the cheese? It works wi' vegan, just takes a bit longer. I'll show ye.'

Shona left them to it. Soon enough, she heard Becca laughing at something James had said.

Although it was a busy Friday night, control agreed to send out a patrol. Shona was doubly pleased to hear the Two Kirsties were on shift and now heading to Kirkness. She'd turned the volume down on the door buzzer, but the flashing light told her either the fans or the photographers were repeatedly pressing it anyway, in the hope James might appear.

She wanted to ask him how Michael Vincent's funeral had gone, if there'd been any trouble on the way back to the house, or if anything out of the ordinary had happened, but there would be time for that later. Mostly, she just wanted to understand what had happened in the garden. It could be someone looking for James but, compared to the complexity and showmanship of the Burns Supper attack, this was clumsy. However, that could also be an indication that the attacker's behaviour was beginning to escalate into something more chaotic.

What does he think he's up to?

The other explanation was that Rob had been the target. Someone had been watching and knew about Shona's meeting with Katherine 'Kanga' Jones. What did *Rob* think he was up to? He'd been told not to appeal. It was both a threat and a warning. If Delfont could get to them even behind the high fences and beefed-up security of High Pines, they weren't safe anywhere.

She jumped as her phone buzzed in her hand. Thalia Brookes was calling.

Shona quickly checked on James and Becca, then closed the door between the kitchen and the utility room.

'I've got something,' Thalia said, her voice alive with excitement. 'I looked into companies registered to addresses in the Craylands estate. I found one, Pearl Holdings. Company director: Margaret Lobel. That name mean anything to you?'

Shona's attention was only half on what Thalia was saying. 'No, I don't think so.'

'Didn't mean nuthin' to Operation Vita neither.'

Through the utility window, Shona saw the blue lights of the approaching patrol car reflect off the pines. 'There's a connection?'

'I went to the registered address. It's a flat above a pizza place. Remember that name your contact gave you, Ethan Brown? Ain't his real name. He's Ernie Brown, small-time con artist. I found him living at the flat. Last few years ain't been kind to him. Seems Delfont arrested Brown for petty theft and recruited him to pose as an intern. And get this, Delfont's mother did a runner. Pearl was the name of the woman who brought Delfont up.'

Shona's attention shot back to Thalia. 'This company have any assets?'

'You're gonna love this, babes. Sole asset is a house in the Lake District, on the shores of Derwentwater, worth a cool £3 million.'

Thalia's excitement was catching, and Shona's heart lifted at the idea they might, finally, be making progress.

'But we still have to make the link to Delfont.'

'Oh, we will, 'cos guess where he and the missus are currently holidaying? I'll give you a clue. It ain't a caravan in Southend.'

'You're kidding?' Shona's mind was racing. 'He can't be that stupid.'

'Stupid or confident,' Thalia replied. 'We know it happens. CPS have just dropped the rape cases. Your Rob is inside. I'm on leave for stress and will probably get medically retired. What's he got to worry about?'

But perhaps Delfont did have something to worry about. If he'd sent someone up to Kirkness to make threats in person, it meant she and Thalia were on the right track.

'We need more to nail this down,' Shona said.

'I know how we'll get more,' Thalia said, her voice hardening. 'Let's ask him.'

'What?' Shona was stunned. 'He's never going to admit to anything. He's a DCI. No way he'll let anything slip.'

'I didn't say we'd ask nicely. Come on, Shona, wouldn't you like five minutes on your own with him when you weren't off your face from a chemical cosh?'

Having spent so long under threat from Delfont, Shona would almost welcome a showdown. But she knew she couldn't go down that route. Ultimately, revenge wasn't justice.

'Look, Thalia, we've got a real line of enquiry here. I've a friend on the force in Cumbria. Let me ask him to do some digging. Delfont's smart enough not to use bank cards for that address. We just need a witness. Delfont paying a local cash in hand for a job on the house. He's mean enough to do that. I'm sure if there's anything, my contact will find it. Just hold on, we're nearly there.'

Shona went back into the kitchen, a bounce in her step, but she knew the closer she got to Delfont, the bigger the threat would be. Ric and Ben were good, but James was their focus. She was worried that whoever had attacked Becca would come back tonight for another go. They had the radio to summon help, but Shona wasn't taking any chances.

'I want you to sleep in with me tonight, Becca,' she said. 'You can bring whichever ridiculous fluffy toy you fancy.'

'Muuum. Embarrassing!' Becca's eyes slid to James, but he just grinned and munched his fried-cheese sandwich, offering Shona the one already on the table.

Any toy except that bloody kangaroo, Shona thought. She was already formulating a plan to dispose of it without Becca realising. A move in small increments to the bottom of the pile, then the bin. If only all her problems were so easily solved.

Chapter 26

Shona slept little that night. It seemed for a while that Becca wouldn't settle either, but the brush with the attacker and the aftermath had clearly exhausted her, and she was soon asleep, lying on her back with one arm flung above her head, like she knew the answer to whatever question she'd been asked.

At some point, Shona must have drifted off herself. She woke in the thin light of early morning, wishing she knew the answers to questions of her own. The more she considered the assailant's words to Becca, *what does he think he's up to*, the more she believed they referred to Rob and his prospective appeal. That ultimately it was Delfont who was behind the attack. But would Detective Superintendent Davies see it that way? She doubted it. She could tell Rob, but that would only strengthen his view that he was doing the right thing by lying low. She hadn't even confided in Thalia, knowing it would only increase her friend's conviction that they should confront Delfont. Shona was caught between the two.

She'd called Dan last night, straight after talking to Thalia, and asked him to look into the ownership of the Lake District house. He knew her history with Delfont and what Rob's court case had cost her, and immediately agreed to help. When her phone buzzed under her pillow, she thought it must be him. Becca stirred next to her, so she got out of bed, pulled on a hoodie over her pyjamas and hurried downstairs.

But it wasn't Dan's name on the phone display.

'Shona, it's me. Callum. Are you wantin' yer mail? 'Cos I might get torn tae bits if I stand here much longer.'

In the background Shona could hear the familiar cacophony of fans. Uniform had removed the last of them just before midnight, but they'd obviously come back as soon as the coast was clear. In the kitchen, she reached for the door buzzer. Ben, having come up silently from the lower ground floor, made her jump.

'It's fine, it's just Callum,' Shona assured him. 'He's the postman round here. And he works on the lifeboat with me.'

Ben came out to the gate with her anyway, sizing Callum up. The postman shoved the handful of packages and letters through the gap. Behind him, a dozen fans hoisted their phone cameras, anxious for a glimpse. Shona cringed, as she was out there in her pyjamas and no make-up.

Callum beat a retreat to the van.

Shona texted him. *Thanks, Callum. Sorry!*

She left the pile of mail on the kitchen table and went back upstairs to get showered and dressed, keen not to be caught out again by fans, security, the media or, she was surprised to find herself thinking, by James.

She came back into the kitchen in jeans and a charcoal cashmere sweater, hair dried and straightened, and light make-up in place. She got herself a coffee, texted Becca that it really was time to get out of bed and went into Rob's office.

Although it was Saturday, she knew DC Kate Irving was on-call and would be at Cornwall Mount. She could update Shona on any leads uncovered by uniform on last night's intruder. They could also go over any steps needed to heighten security around James, when filming on the final scenes resumed tomorrow.

Shona tried to keep her attention away from her WhatsApp to stop herself speculating when Dan Ridley in Cumbria would get back to her about Delfont's house. She could feel a mounting excitement that here was the break they needed to nail him. Al Capone was famously taken down by tax evasion charges. Perhaps something as simple as a cash-in-hand payment for tree surgery, or a Deliveroo account, might just be how they'd get Delfont.

Kate answered and Shona pictured her in the quiet weekend CID office. Murdo would be taking Joan shopping or down the rugby club for lunch. Ravi and Martin might be off on a day out somewhere. Suddenly, Shona was aware just how far she'd travelled in the last few months from all that counted as normality. She felt a crushing desire for the reassurance of the mundane, the routine and the ordinary.

'Nothing from uniform about McGowan's stalker,' Kate said. 'They did a house-to-house, but with all the fan activity there's nothing specific.'

Shona had expected as much. She felt guilty for not sharing with Kate the possibility that she, not James, was the target. 'Any sign of the *U will dye* note?'

Kate sighed. 'Nothing. They emptied the bins the day before.'

'Anything new from the attack at the Burns Supper?'

'I've gone back over the witness statements and the Caledonian Hotel's CCTV. Whoever it was, they didn't come in by the main entrance or the lifts, pass reception, or go into the bar. I can't believe no one saw who switched the haggis.'

Shona could. There was no CCTV in the dining room, or the lobby leading to it. It had been a busy night. The hotel was fully booked and there were non-residents in for the Burns Supper.

'None of the guests are unaccounted for?' Shona said.

'We've spoken to them all. There were hospitality agency people in too, but the key thing is the bar staff really only interacted with the other bar staff, and the waiting staff were the same.'

'So, if you were from the bar and you saw someone carrying a covered tray, you'd presume they were waiting staff, and vice versa. Probably wouldn't even register you'd seen the attacker. All he needed to do was come in the back door, do the switch and leave. Five or ten minutes, tops.'

'But how did he know McGowan would be there? Surely something like that takes a bit of planning?'

'Same way the fans knew,' Shona sighed. 'It went on the B&B owners' website the day before. If the *U will dye* note is connected to the incident, then the attacker already had the IED and the dye packs for something else he had planned and improvised. How many places have haggis on sale at this time of year? He could have driven to Glasgow and bought one.'

'After what happened last night, all we can say is that the suspect is a man,' Kate said. 'Is Becca okay?'

'I think so. It helps having Ric and Ben here. I don't know exactly what they've been teaching her when I haven't been around – *desert survival skills*, she called it.'

'And James McGowan?' Kate said, amusement in her voice. 'Is he always in front of the mirror? Or in meltdown? Can't be easy.'

'It's been fine, actually,' Shona said. It was on the tip of her tongue to reveal their previous acquaintance, and in some ways she was surprised that Kate hadn't made the connection. Perhaps it was her Edinburgh upbringing and lack of knowledge of Glasgow geography. Ravi would have spotted it, if he hadn't been tied up with the fatal house fire. She tried not to compare her DCs unfavourably. Their skill sets were different, and that's what made them good for the team. After three years of working together, they knew each other's foibles inside out and their competitiveness kept them sharp.

'You know,' Shona began, 'I think if anyone can identify the attacker, it's the fans. They literally run twenty-four-hour surveillance on James… and each other, I suspect. There's so much rivalry there.'

'We talked to them at the hotel,' Kate said, doubtfully. 'They didn't give us anything.'

'Well, I've got them camped on my doorstep, so let's see if we can turn that into a positive. Come out here for a coffee. They know I've been on the set, and that James is living in my house. Perhaps that'll be enough to get them at least talking.'

'You think you've built a relationship with them?'

They've seen me in my pyjamas, Shona thought. That probably constitutes a relationship.

'We're not going to find that *U will dye* note now,' Shona said. 'So, until we get something back on the IED, a witness is potentially our best hope.'

Shona ended the call. There was the smell of a vegetarian full Scottish breakfast drifting up from the guest suites, and she wondered if she might be cheeky and cadge a few sausages and maybe an egg for a sandwich. She'd just heard Becca go into the kitchen and, by the sound of crockery and pans, start on porridge. But after such a disturbed night, Shona needed something savoury and protein-based to see her through the morning, and a potentially nerve-shredding encounter with James's wired fans.

'Mum!' Becca's call had an urgency and sharpness to it that brought Ben once more up from the guest suite. He paused on the landing, looking enquiringly at Shona before they both crossed to the kitchen.

Becca stood by the kitchen table and, at first, Shona couldn't see what was amiss. She was just about to conclude that Becca had seen a spider or suffered a minor burn, when she followed her daughter's gaze to the pile of mail.

There, on the table next to an open, padded envelope, lay three bullets.

Ben went to the stairs and let out a short, sharp whistle. A moment later, Ric appeared.

'Are you hurt?' Shona said, trying to reconcile the sight of bullets on her kitchen table, in her home. 'Did you touch them?'

Becca shook her head as she allowed her mother to put a comforting arm around her.

'I just dropped them on the table. They're meant for James, aren't they? Why is someone doing this?'

'It's probably just a sick joke,' Shona said, fooling neither Becca nor herself.

There was no name on the front of the envelope, just *High Pines* in thick, black marker, followed by the address and what looked like a smudged London postmark, dated for the day before. Carried unwittingly by Callum and having passed through numerous other hands, they'd get nothing forensically from the outside. The bullets themselves were 9mm pistol calibre and the faint, sharp smell told her they'd likely been wiped clean of prints and DNA with alcohol.

'Why three bullets?' Ric said, watching Shona carefully.

He was part of Lilly Chase's security team. He had to know the whole story: why Shona was running the business on her own, and where her husband was.

'Ben, mate,' he said, eyes still on Shona. 'Take Becca downstairs a minute. Make her a hot chocolate and get her to show you how to set the clock on the microwave.' He turned, smiling, to Shona's daughter. 'Unplugged it at the wall, didn't he, the dozy doughnut. Sort him out, will ya?'

Becca wasn't fooled, but she got that some aspects of her mother's work and the threat to James McGowan weren't for open discussion. She followed Ben out of the kitchen without protest.

'So? Why three bullets?' Ric said again, eyebrows raised, stare intense, and Shona knew she'd have a hard time getting anything past him. 'One would be enough for Jamie boy to get the message.' He dropped his voice. 'Now, I don't presume to tell you how to do your job, but this don't seem like someone who's messing about. James is my number-one priority but you and Becca ain't far behind, so whatever's goin' on, it affects everyone in this house, 'cos if someone's coming in here armed, you need to tell me now, girl.'

When Shona didn't answer, he went on, in a gentler tone, 'I grew up with my old man inside. I know it ain't easy for them that's left to get on with things. You're a copper. Your fella is in prison. What sorta mess 'as he got himself into, then?'

Shona looked past Ric to where James was standing. She didn't know how long he'd been there or what he'd overheard. Ric seemed to sense without turning that the actor was behind him. He gave Shona a look that said he knew he'd hit the mark and expected full disclosure – if not now, then soon.

James's eyes travelled from Shona to the bullets on the table and back again, and she saw something familiar in his expression that caused the years to drop away. Suddenly, they were back on the scheme, complicit in their under-standing that there was no way out of this situation that didn't have consequences – bad ones. Shona turned away, confused by the ease with which she'd slipped back to a place where she had less sense of agency or control.

'DC Kate Irving is on her way over.' Shona pulled open a kitchen drawer and tore a large freezer bag from a roll. With a pair of plastic gloves, she swept the bullets and envelope into the makeshift evidence container. 'She'll send them to forensics.'

Ric folded his arms but when Shona remained tight-lipped, he turned and stomped back downstairs with a look that said he'd be back once she'd thought better of it.

She went out to the utility room, grasping the worktop and drawing in deep breaths to steady herself. But when she went back into the kitchen to start breakfast, James hadn't followed Ric back downstairs as she'd believed. He was leaning against the sink, arms folded, as if waiting for her return.

'Whoever those bullets are meant fur – you or me – we're in this together. Tell me how I can help. I willnae judge, you know that. You've already put yer life on the line for me. Don't think I wouldn't do the same for you.'

Despite the infancy of their reacquaintance, she knew he spoke from the heart, for their comradeship had been forged in an early bond you could only share with your own folk.

'Thank you,' she said, quietly.

Right now, she couldn't articulate the complexity of what she was feeling. Any conversation about Delfont and Rob and all her troubles would have to wait for another time. But when he opened his arms, Shona found it was the easiest thing in the world to step into them, just for a moment.

Chapter 27

After she'd eaten a bowl of porridge and drunk two cups of coffee, Shona felt more herself.

It was a cowardly act to send bullets by post. If they'd been shoved though the letterbox, it would suggest the prowler who'd grabbed Becca was sending the message – as Ric had suggested – that he was armed.

But whoever had posted the bullets was in London, not lurking close by. The two incidents were either not related or being orchestrated to exert repeated pressure. It meant Thalia might also be in danger.

Shona tried her number, and once more got Thalia's voicemail. What if something had already happened to her, or it had just got too much and she'd killed herself, as Delfont's other victim had done? Shona couldn't bear to think of such a thing happening, but she didn't know of anyone she could call to check on Thalia's welfare.

After a pause, she texted a carefully phrased message that there'd been developments and particular care was needed, and Thalia must make contact immediately to tell Shona she was all right. Delfont was marking Shona's card. The meaning was clear. You and your family are in my gunsights. But if she thought about it too much, she'd never step out the door, and she couldn't let that monster imprison her.

Where her daughter was concerned, it was a different matter. Even the smallest of risks was too much. Becca appeared to be bearing up comparatively well and Shona began to realise that this was what past traumas had given Becca. Not vulnerability, but resilience.

When Kate arrived at the gate, Ben gave her the once-over — a look that travelled up and down in a way it hadn't with Callum. Kate shook back her blonde hair in response. Shona understood the reaction. Ben was attractive. Quieter than Ric, more watchful. Kate was single. Shona wasn't sure about Ben. As former SBS — Special Boat Service — perhaps he conformed to the stereotype of a girl in every port.

With that thought, Rob's affair flooded back into her head. She remembered Katherine Jones's expression as she'd passed the file across the table in Tebay Services. She was magnanimous in giving Shona back her husband, contrite in her admission of wrongdoing without ever owning the damage she'd done. It was, Shona decided, all bullshit.

Shona passed Kate the freezer bag containing the bullets and envelope, their conversation business-like. Kate tutted and Shona let her believe there was no question that James McGowan had been the intended recipient of the threat. Any alternative interpretations could wait until after forensic evidence said different.

They took their coffees, the walkie-talkie handset linked to James's security, and Kate's laptop upstairs to the lounge. Beyond the windows, the sea and sky were parallel bands of grey. Shona self-consciously moved Rob's files from the table. They sat down, side by side, and Kate opened a document that listed the forty or so fans already interviewed, complete with headshots taken from their social media.

Shona scrolled through it. 'This is very thorough. Well done.'

'Chloe and Vinny helped,' Kate replied, her cheeks tinged pink with pleasure at the approval from a boss she often felt was over-picky with her work.

'Anyone stand out for you?' Shona said.

'There's a couple, boss,' Kate replied, pulling the laptop towards her. She brought up a face Shona instantly recognised as Crop-Top, the temperature-impervious woman who'd approached her on her first day on set, and who was among the current group besieging High Pines.

Kate tapped the screen with her index finger. 'Callie McGowan. No relation to James McGowan. Changed her name from Rivers by deed poll, ten years ago. She's thirty-six years old, from Hemel Hempstead. Single, no children. Rented studio flat. Employment record shows a series of part-time jobs, but she seems to be funding herself from the sale of her parents' house. Follows McGowan everywhere in the UK when he's here. Very active on forums, considers herself his number one fan. Social media full of older selfies with him, but recently not so much, but that's the same across the board. I guess he's been warned against them.'

'Restraining order?' Shona said, thinking of the litany of transgressions by fans that James had mentioned. The escalating nature of those alone would put you off doing selfies, and perhaps that might feel like a rejection to an intimacy-seeking individual.

Kate made a face. 'No restraining order. Her behaviour has always stopped short of that. His management company consider her a pest and Herefordshire Police spoke to her about a fight with another fan over a signed T-shirt McGowan donated at a charity auction.'

'Right,' said Shona, finishing her coffee and motioning Kate to do the same. 'Callie Rivers McGowan is where we start.'

She picked up the VHF handset and told Ric they were going outside, turning down his offer of a minder, as getting close to the fans was exactly what she hoped to do.

'I ain't happy about you ladies going out there on your own.'

It was a reasonable response, given the situation, and Kate did seem to perk up at the idea Ben might be joining them. Shona felt it would be churlish to remind Ric that *the ladies* were both trained CID officers, given that he was aware of the true risk she was facing. As a concession, she confided her plan to interview the fans informally as potential witnesses to both the Burns Supper incident and Becca's attack, and relay anything useful. They would stay within sight of the gate. She added that Becca was in her room, they'd had a chat and she understood the gravity of the situation, a coded admission that Shona did too.

Ric reluctantly grunted his consent, reminding them to *look lively*.

Shona intended to do just that. The stalker circling closer and the contents of this morning's post fresh in her mind, she wasn't about to take any chances.

–

Shona slid back the bolt on the gate. There was a vibration in the air, like the quivering of birds' wings, then a cacophony of crow-like calls: *James. James. James.*

Shona scanned the crowd for any identifiable threat but found none. There was no press that Shona could see, and that suited her purpose. She greeted the disappointed fans with smiles and enquiries after their welfare, hoping the woman she'd shoved the previous evening wasn't among the group and, if she was, that she didn't bear a grudge. She spotted Callie in the crowd, phone camera raised and thrusting her doll–like elbows into the faces of her neighbours.

Shona held up a hand to still the questions, then she spoke in a warm, clear voice.

'James has asked me to say thank you for all your good wishes.' She paused, making eye contact with as many fans as she could. 'In light of recent events, he's been advised by his security team to remain inside. He knows you'll understand.' She paused again, a look of sympathetic regret. 'As many of you know, my name is Detective Inspector Shona Oliver and if you've any concerns about what's been happening, please come and talk to me.'

Feet were shuffled and some fans murmured to each other. It was like facing a particularly sullen school assembly. Undeterred, Shona searched out the group she'd seen outside the Burns museum in Dumfries.

'Ah, Ms McGowan, there you are,' she said in her best headmistress voice. 'Can I have a word?'

Just the use of the McGowan name had a talismanic effect. Heads turned towards Callie, who basked in the attention, curiosity aroused. Might James have a special message for her? The crowd seemed to part as she moved forward, her posture straightening by the second as she felt the warmth of others' attention shining upon her.

'Detective Shona,' she said, offering her thin hand and tilting her head to one side in a way that was both demure and calculating.

'Callie, you don't mind if I call you Callie, do you?' Shona said and waited for the woman to nod her consent. 'This is DC Kate Irving.' She ushered her constable forward, then lowered her voice, conspiratorially. 'Kate is working with the American police on tracing whoever's behind these shocking online attacks on James. We know you're his number one fan. We'd…' Shona paused. '*He'd…* really appreciate your help.'

Shona could practically see the hunger spark in Callie's face, as she worked out what could be extracted in exchange for her co-operation. Other fans were nudging closer, anxious to hear any titbit. The side-flick of Callie's eyes betrayed she was aware of them too. She walked a few steps further from the gate, beckoning Shona and Kate to follow, which they dutifully did.

'Who's doing these awful things to James?' Shona said abruptly, calculating Callie couldn't return to the other fans so quickly without losing face.

'How should I know?' The woman looked suddenly much younger than her thirty-six years, as if she'd remained stuck in adolescence, which in a way she had.

'You're his number one fan,' Shona said, putting her on the spot. 'James could have been really badly injured at the Burns Supper. Whoever did that had to be close. Listen to me, Callie, this stalker is trying to take everything away from James. They're trying to destroy his career and force him out of acting, and you may be the only one who can stop that. What does his number one fan know that can help him?'

Shona held her breath. It sounded so over the top that she feared she'd gone too far.

Callie was staring, wide-eyed. She reached out and grasped Shona's hand.

Shona calculated that one of two things might happen. If this woman was behind any of the attacks, then this was the moment she'd confess, linking her name with McGowan's forever, more closely than a deed-poll form ever could. It would be like Vanda had said in the case of John Lennon's assassin. Google James McGowan, and Callie's name would be there somewhere in the results.

'There was someone,' Callie said slowly.

It was the second option. Callie, her crown as number one fan in jeopardy, would plumb her memory for some detail that would stop it toppling. That was all Shona needed.

'He's one of the extras. He's got this big white beard. Weird guy. Hangs around sometimes. Keeps saying he knows stuff about James. Like he'd know more than me,' Callie said, scornfully.

Somehow, Shona had been expecting a woman, but a man would fit with Becca's attacker, if the incident had indeed been about James.

'Was he there the night of the Burns Supper?' Shona said, aware that Kate was also listening intently. Some of the other fans had shuffled close.

'Oh, him,' a voice came from close by. 'He's hit on me too. Asking, did I want to go for a drink, and he'd tell me all about the filming. Creepy.'

It was the round-faced girl from the set, a look of smug satisfaction as if she'd delivered the punchline to someone else's joke.

Callie glared at her, but the others were crowding around now, eager to add their voice to the chorus and do their bit for James. All of them agreed this man was a pest. Not a true fan. But Callie was not to be outdone.

'He *was* outside the hotel on the night of the Burns Supper, Detective Shona,' she said smugly.

The others stopped and looked at Callie. When she had their full attention, she smiled at Shona and, like the number one fan repositioning her crown, said, 'His name's Brian Aston.'

Chapter 28

Such was the chatter and excitement from the fans who crowded around Callie, that they barely noticed Shona and Kate slip back inside the gate.

'What d'you think?' Kate asked when they reached the kitchen.

Shona sat down heavily. 'Oh, I know who he is all right. Seems I overestimated the fans' surveillance abilities.' She pointed to the kettle, inviting Kate to switch it on. Shona opened up her laptop, then turned the screen, showing Aston's file from the extras agency, to face her detective constable.

It appeared that Brian Aston, the full-bearded smuggler extra who'd engaged her in a conversation about time travel in the pub scene on Hildan Island, had been using his film connection to inveigle himself with the female fans.

Had Aston been trying to hit on her, too? Or Becca? Her daughter hadn't reported any issues, and Shona hadn't got that vibe from him, but he'd known she was a cop. Maybe he was sizing her up to check if he was on her radar. That suggested he had previous.

Shit. This was all she needed – another sexual predator on her hands. CID were stretched, but she couldn't just ignore it.

'So, you don't think he's our man?' Kate said, once Shona had explained who he was.

'No,' Shona said, flatly. 'And I'd hate to think any of those lassies thought he was their man either.' She shuddered at the thought of his tombstone teeth. 'He's no threat to James, just the fans. We've a group of infatuated, lonely women desperate to outdo each other. How far d'you think they'd go if someone like Aston offered an inside track, maybe a visit to the film set or a piece of James's clothing, in exchange for sexual favours? I mean, would you?'

Kate looked again at the photo Shona had brought up from Aston's extras agency profile. The straggle of greasy grey hair, florid complexion with snakes of broken veins across his drinker's nose and bushy white beard. It was her turn to shudder.

'Not even for a date with Jason Momoa,' Kate said. 'D'you think he might have crossed the line into coercion or even assault?'

Shona sighed. The reality was, they didn't have the resources to chase every low-grade Lothario they came across. But then she thought of her ex-boss. The behaviour of sexual offenders often began with lesser misdemeanours, before escalating. Maybe if someone had stopped Delfont earlier then she, Thalia, the woman who'd killed herself – and who knew how many other victims – would have been spared.

'Talk to the fans again, individually this time,' Shona said. 'Ashton appears to be an experienced movie extra, but if there's even a hint he's pushed his luck, I'll speak to the director, Simon Jones, and get him off that set. Talk to his agency and check his employment record. Find out if this is his regular MO, and if there's been previous complaints about any sex-for-access. And even if none of James's fans lodge an official complaint, he needs his card marking.'

She didn't have the time to do it herself, but she knew just the lassies for the job. A visit from the Two Kirsties – in uniform, rolling up in a marked police vehicle to the camper van site where Aston and most of the extras were based – would send a highly visible message that the police had their eye on him, so he'd better behave.

'My other, more immediate, concern is if the extras have been mixing with the fans, it's a big security risk.' Shona got up and spooned instant coffee into two mugs.

'None of the attacks have actually been on the set, boss,' Kate said.

'True,' Shona conceded. 'But if information on James's movements or security arrangements has been leaking out, that's a gap I want plugged. The background actors were given strict instructions not to talk to the press or fans about any aspect of the film. It's in their contracts.' She knew this because she'd scanned Becca's, initially to make sure there was no hidden nudity clause, or other nasty surprise in it. 'I'll talk to Simon, and the extras agency. Give them all a rocket myself, if I have to.'

She placed a mug in front of Kate and sat back down, cradling her own.

'Leaving aside the armed man who got into his house in Hollywood, since James arrived here, a close friend has gone over a cliff wearing his coat.' Shona ticked the points off on her fingers. 'An IED meant for him was planted but, luckily, failed to detonate. And there's an internet campaign to destroy his reputation.'

Kate tactfully didn't remind her boss that Vincent's death was likely an accident, but added, 'Don't forget the intruder last night and the bullets, boss.'

'Of course,' Shona said, realising she had unconsciously excluded them. 'My point is, if this is the work of one person, it's a skilfully orchestrated campaign.'

Before Kate could answer, her work phone rang. As the on-call detective, she was being summoned. Shona sipped her coffee and tried not to make a face at the taste of the disgusting brew. She needed to go downstairs and update Ric, Ben and James on what she'd learned. Anyway, their coffee was better.

'Yeah, I will,' Kate was saying, grinning. 'I'm at Wee Sh—'

Wee Shona's – that's what she'd been going to say before realising she could be overheard by Wee Shona herself.

'I'm with the boss now,' Kate corrected. Then she tilted her chin towards her DI and said, 'The counterfeit iPad smugglers... The Glasgow cops have got them.'

Shona could have punched the air. Tommy's tip about the van had come good.

'You'd better get off,' Shona said when Kate had hung up.

'I'll get the evidence bag with the bullets and envelope to forensics.'

'Great. But before you go...' She beckoned Kate to follow her upstairs. 'There's something I want you to look at quickly.'

Once back in the lounge, Shona stood at the window and pointed to the *Ramsey Ranger*, which was still moored up in front of the lifeboat station.

'Let Murdo know that you received an anonymous tip. Get a warrant to search that yacht. With luck, you'll find hidden compartments and prints that'll match the fake iPad boxes seized in Glasgow.'

Kate stared at her. 'Don't you want to call this in yourself?'

'It's your case, DC Irving. Like I said, anonymous tip. Now off you go. With any luck, you'll be able to celebrate a result soon.'

And maybe, Shona thought, Sonya Nicolson will get the result she deserves, too.

-

After Kate had left, Shona updated Ric, who delivered a short, expletive-filled assessment of background artists who didn't do what they'd been told. Shona couldn't argue with the sentiment.

She'd liked to have spoken to James personally, but noticed his door was closed and stifled her disappointment.

When she went back up to the lounge, she found to her surprise that he was sitting on the floor with his back against the sofa, looking out over the firth, the Robert Burns volume open on his lap. Becca was next to him, her own pile of books at her side. Neither had heard Shona come in.

'But Burns was an eco-poet in the Romantic tradition of Rousseau,' James said. 'He knew what he wis talkin' about. A ploughman, remember? Toiled the land. His political views took account of the relationship between people and the natural world. He hoped his work would foster a harmony, a balance between the two, like he wis a kind of interpreter. When folk talked of his talent, he said, *tis Nature's powers inspire*.'

Becca nodded. 'So he'd be upset about all the dead geese in the Solway?'

'He'd be raging. Don't you think?'

Shona saw Becca nod. 'I'm raging too. I'm part of a conservation group restoring marshland.'

'Good! Be passionate about wit you believe in. You know, when the Duke of Atholl cut down ancient trees for Royal Navy ships, Burns wrote a public letter urging him tae replace them, and the duke did. Early habitat restoration project.' James flicked the pages of his book and showed Becca a passage. 'You should read *On The Destruction of Drumlanrig Woods* for your essay. Burns called the Duke of Queensberry a *worm* and a *reptile* in print for cutting down Drumlanrig. That sort o' thing got your head kicked in back then.'

'Cool guy,' Becca said.

'Supercool. It's why I wanted to make the film about him. So, who can I talk to about supporting habitat work locally? We can tie it to the film's release.'

'I can ask my group. Or Kyle, the RSPB warden.'

'Can you do that for me?'

'Sure.'

Shona smiled and was about to tiptoe back to the kitchen and leave them to their discussion, when she saw Becca put down her notebook and curl her legs up in front of her, chin on her knees. 'You know who else is supercool? My mum.'

'Super, supercool, your mum,' James agreed, his eyes on the far bank of the estuary, giving nothing away.

'What was she like at school?' Becca said.

'She was amazing at art, could really draw.'

Becca sat up straight. 'Really?'

Shona hadn't picked up a sketchpad in years, so Becca was right to be surprised.

'When did you first meet her?'

'Fourth Year play. Shakespeare wis a hard sell at our school, so they roped in the third years. Yer mum must have been fourteen, maybe. She was a stunner. Beautiful eyes.'

'Mum did Shakespeare?'

'Portia's speech from *The Merchant of Venice*. "The quality of mercy is not strained." See, she was all about the application of the law even then.' He grinned.

How on earth had he remembered that? She'd found the whole episode embarrassing but he'd known who she was before Shona was even aware of his existence.

'You like her, don't you?'

Shona heard the mischievous teasing in Becca's voice. She thought now was the time to break up this little chat, but she held her breath, curious as to what James might say to her daughter. The sun had sunk low in the west, turning both figures into silhouettes, their faces becoming shadowed and unreadable.

'Course I like your mum,' James said, then paused. 'Think she likes me?'

'Naw,' Becca teased. 'Why would she?'

'Why would she indeed?' he replied, with a tone of defeat, which was, Shona thought, less comic than he'd intended.

Becca laughed, relenting. 'Actually, she thinks you're okay.' For a moment she was silent, then her voice became serious. 'You know my dad's in jail?'

Shona saw James nod.

'My mum's had a really tough time of it, so you better not give her any shit.'

'Your mum and I go way back, Becca. I wouldnae upset her for the world.'

'Good,' said Becca. 'Just make sure you don't. Now, are you any good at maths?'

'I'm shit at maths,' James said.

'Right,' said Becca, getting up. 'Well, you're no use to me. I'll need to text Martin, he understands that stuff. And thanks, by the way.'

'What for?' James asked.

'The essay and everything. Just… thanks.'

–

Shona slipped back downstairs to her bedroom and closed the door. She needed a moment to compose herself. When he'd hugged her in the kitchen, it had been as a friend, hadn't it? *Think she likes me?* If only she could have seen his face. *Think she likes me?* For fuck's sake, they weren't in the playground now. There was no mystery. They'd got off on the wrong foot. James was checking bridges had been mended, that was all. Focus on the job, Shona. She stood by the window. It was the same view it always had been, but it felt changed. The *Ramsey Ranger* had spun on its mooring with the tide and now faced the open sea. She remembered the phone call Kate had received, and savoured the idea that at least the net was closing around Larry Smith and his gang. No way he'd fancy a stint in prison at his age. He'd likely give up the others in exchange for a lighter sentence.

Once the evidence was stacked up against Smith, his threat to Tommy would evaporate. If he claimed that the Kirkness lifeboat helm had prior knowledge of drug smuggling he'd only implicate himself, and a longer custodial sentence would be guaranteed. All Tommy had to do was sit tight.

She was just about to dial his number, when she spotted the telltale streak of orange heading at speed out of Kirkness estuary towards the firth. She opened the crew app on her phone and saw: *ILB launch 12:52*.

Tommy's phone went straight to voicemail. She felt the double frustration of not being able to update him on the *Ramsey Ranger* and missing out on a shout.

The boxes of Rob's papers lay on the floor. She picked up the files and scanned half-heartedly through them. What was the point, if Rob was just going to shoot down her efforts?

Unfortunate phrase, she told herself, given this morning's delivery. And what else was he hiding from her? It hadn't taken her long to notice there appeared to be different versions of the same documents, and the files that the prosecution had disclosed to Anoushka didn't tally with what Katherine Jones had kept as her insurance against dismissal.

Had Rob discovered the money laundering much earlier than he claimed, and instead of reporting it, tried to cover it up? Had he perjured himself?

Shit, she thought. No wonder he didn't want her digging around in the case.

She spent a few more minutes staring at the remaining boxes, before throwing the papers aside and running downstairs to the guest suites. Ric and Ben were cutting thick slabs of focaccia and layering them with roasted vegetables and mozzarella. It smelled amazing. She marvelled at what they could turn out from a basic microwave and hotplate arrangement. Becca needed to get their creations on Insta. Through the open door of the neighbouring suite, she saw James, shirtless, lying on the bed.

'There's a shout. I'm needed at the lifeboat station,' she said to Ric and Ben, trying not to make it sound like she was asking permission. Even if she wasn't out on the *Margaret Wilson*, she could support the shore crew.

From the corner of her eye, she saw James remove his headphones and get up. He pulled a T-shirt on and came out to join them.

'Is Shona gonna be safe?' he asked the men.

'I'll be indoors and surrounded by the other volunteers,' she reassured him, feeling a little overwhelmed by his concern for her wellbeing. How far she'd drifted from the sensation of being cared for. How lonely she'd become. She gave James a quick grateful smile.

Ric tilted his head to his partner, indicating he should go with her. Ben wordlessly put down his untouched focaccia and picked up his jacket.

'Becca got the tin can?' Ric said, referring to the walkie-talkie Shona had dropped in with her daughter on the way past her room.

Shona nodded.

'Oi, Bravo Oscar,' Ric said, into his handset. 'Lunch.' He turned to Shona. 'You want Ben to stay with ya?' When she said it wasn't necessary, he continued. 'Just watch yourself and let us know when you're ready to come back.'

He handed her a third walkie-talkie, which Shona tucked into her fleece.

'Okay,' she said. 'But I want you to buzz me if there's any trouble.'

'Righto,' Ric agreed, picking up a plate and, with a flip of his spatula, depositing an expertly toasted focaccia, which he held out to James. He seemed to sense the actor's anxiety. 'She can handle herself, mate. Best if you stay put.'

–

In the end, Shona didn't need to tell Tommy there'd been developments with the *Ramsey Ranger*; he saw it for himself. By the time the lifeboat was making its way back to the Kirkness slipway, Murdo had got his warrant and the yacht was crawling with scenes of crime officers. On the quayside sat Murdo's Astra, a squad car, the forensic van and an unmarked vehicle that Shona guessed belonged to Trading Standards.

The lifeboat station's shore crew had observed the activity and quizzed her, but she'd feigned ignorance. As the tractor and trailer drew into the boat hall, Tommy caught Shona's eye, and she did her best to look calm and reassuring.

'Any sign of Larry Smith?' she asked quietly, after Tommy had changed out of his drysuit and come upstairs to complete the debrief.

He took the tea she held out to him and shook his head.

The rest of the crew were discussing the shout with Callum and Gordon Fraser, an agricultural student and new recruit on his first real call-out, who looked thrilled and relieved to have assisted with a stranded kite surfer near Southerness Lighthouse.

'Smith's not been back,' Tommy said, quietly. 'But I'm ready to face the music if I have to. It'd be a betrayal of all I've stood for if I didnae do everything I can tae put an end to this.'

'It won't come to that, Tommy,' Shona said, unsure if he meant the blackmail or the smuggling in general.

'You'll need to give a statement, since you worked on the yacht, and say if you've any idea where Larry Smith is, but that'll be all.'

Tommy narrowed his eyes and blew on his tea.

'Have you any idea?' Shona pressed.

'Mibbaes,' Tommy replied, quietly.

'Then leave it to the police, Trading Standard, Customs,' Shona said, anxiously. 'They're all on it. It's fine if you just walk away.'

'Aye, of course,' he said. But she knew that determined look. It had got them out of many a tight spot but now she feared it would lead Tommy straight into another very tight spot indeed. And there was nothing she could say to stop it.

—

That evening, Shona found it impossible to settle. She was anxious about Tommy, worried that he'd take the law into his own hands and pursue Larry Smith around the ports of the Irish Sea. She kept glancing down from the lounge, checking the *Silver Crest* was still visible on its mooring, a dark outline next to the *Ranger*, which blazed with light from the SOCOs' lamps. Dan still hadn't got back to her about Delfont's house, except for a text to say he was working on it. Her repeated calls to Thalia went straight to voicemail. The other woman's phone was switched off. It was out of character for Thalia not to return her calls, or at least text.

Ric, Ben and James had come up to the lounge to discuss the security plans for tomorrow's filming of the final scenes, and play a few rounds of cards with Becca. Shona had called Simon Jones and he'd assured her the extras and crew would be reminded in the strongest terms about their confidentiality clause, and face dismissal and forfeit of fees if they were found to have broken it.

James insisted on showing the two men his handiwork repairing the lamp, turning it on and off until Shona was sure the coastguard would be paying them a visit to establish that they weren't signalling to smugglers out in the Solway. Ric and Ben looked suitably impressed. In that small moment of normality, Shona recognised a sweetness all the more potent for its rarity.

He caught her smile. 'I know. Pathetic, isn't it?'

'Daniel Day-Lewis makes furniture,' Ric offered.

'And I heard Harrison Ford built a house,' Ben replied.

'Now, Michael Caine' – Ric exaggerated his cockney accent in a fair impression of the actor – 'what a lot of people don't know is, he's a brilliant plumber. Invite him round for supper, and he'll be straight in your en-suite changing a washer.'

'Yeah, yeah, guys. Very funny,' James said, with a sardonic smile. 'You're supposed to protect me, no' demolish me.'

'Ah, now, if you're talking demolition, Whoopi Goldberg's your girl,' Ric said. 'Took out a wall and re-laid the bricks herself. Flemish bond, quick as you like. Saw it with me own eyes.'

Becca was at the low coffee table, shuffling the cards and snorting with laughter.

'See what I have tae put up wi',' James appealed to Shona, but she was laughing too.

After the events of the previous days, it felt good to let go and she suddenly reflected on how much she'd misjudged or, perhaps more accurately, mis-remembered him. It was as if they'd picked up where they'd left off more than twenty years before. This was the Jazza she'd known, quick to smile, eager to please, happy to be the butt of jokes. He thought she hadn't changed, and perhaps, she reflected, no one really does.

They played cards until Ric, Ben and James said they'd head back downstairs to get things ready for the morning and the final day of filming. Shona cleared away the dishes and set the kitchen straight, letting Becca drift up to her room. When she passed Becca's door, the light was off, and she felt relieved that her daughter was coping so well.

But for Shona, it was not so easy. Despite the relaxing turn the evening had taken, she was far from sleep and paced the room. She thought again of her run with James out to Knockie Point – the freedom and exhilaration she'd experienced – and wished they could do that now.

Just as she was getting to know him again, he was slipping away. There were so many things they hadn't talked about. It wasn't clear when he and his security detail would be leaving, but it could only be a day or so away. Once James McGowan had gone, Detective Superintendent Davies would breathe a sigh of relief, but did Shona feel the same? Suddenly, the stuffiness of her bedroom was too much to bear. She'd walk herself to exhaustion, even if it was just around the garden.

She left by the utility room, locking the door behind her and taking the steps down the side of the house.

The door of one of the guest suites was ajar, and suddenly there was a shadow. Her breath caught, but the shape made no move to silence her. She thought it must be Ric or Ben, but then she smelled his familiar scent and knew James McGowan had been waiting for her.

It was a conversation in which no words were exchanged: the slightest movement of hands and eyes drew them together. Their breath hung in a single cloud around them.

She moved forward and kissed him. He pulled her inside.

He was kind. He was considerate. He was gentle. He was everything she'd imagined he might be. And when they started, she never wanted to stop.

Chapter 29

If Ric was aware that James McGowan had company the previous night in the guest suite, he didn't acknowledge it to Shona. She'd risen long before dawn, making her way back upstairs via the utility-room door, before anyone was awake.

'Them bullets,' Ric said as they stood by the gate at High Pines, preparing to leave. 'If they were for James, we need to be prepared for something like a sniper threat.'

Shona knew that his warning was meant for her too.

'He's flat-out refusing to wear a vest,' Ric added. He stopped short of asking her to intervene, knowing it would be useless. 'We need to lock that set up tight as a drum.'

Shona agreed, but would it be enough?

There were only a handful of fans at the gate, who waved excitedly as the pair of fourbies sped past them, despite the early hour and the bitter, freezing air.

Her team had been combing through the gifts from fans, social media, and the CCTV and interviews from the Burns Night at the Caledonian Hotel, but they still had no one they could arrest. This was progress, not failure, she'd told her officers and civilian staff, a necessary draining of the pool until their suspect became evident, but she could see their frustration. And was this vindictive individual even now boarding a flight out of the country, to perhaps lie low, content to wait for another, higher profile opportunity – a US film premiere, or a talk show – to taunt, harass and finally kill James? That would be some other police force's responsibility. And while Superintendent Davies might rejoice at that, the thought just brought Shona more anguish.

On the fifteen-minute drive to the location on a private estate near Colvend, they took care to establish that they weren't being followed. James sat in the back of one of the cars, book in hand, lost in preparation. She looked back to their first meeting and realised that what she'd seen as abrasiveness was merely his quest for authenticity. And while James might argue it was the real Burns, she now knew it wasn't the real James.

Shona and Becca travelled with Ben in the other vehicle. There'd been no opportunity for a private moment with James, and Shona had studiously avoided eye contact when they were in company, afraid that anyone observing them would register, by that look alone, the shift in their intimacy.

In Shona's mind there lurked the constant worry that if the stalker could source explosives for an IED, what else were they able to get their hands on? Ric was obviously thinking the same way. He'd brought food from High Pines, which Becca had helped prepare, and warned James not to eat or drink anything else.

When they arrived in the field, the wind was brutal. Shona wrapped her pashmina around her neck, tying it securely. They needed to complete the journey on foot across the marshland to reach the shore, and the cave where the shot was being set up. They walked in single file, in silence – Shona, Becca and James between the two security guards.

Frozen pools lay among the sea grass like shards of shattered mirrors, reflecting the gunmetal sky. Far out across the empty sands, the horizon was no more than a grey smudge. She knew the area, had visited it a dozen times from both the land and the sea but, in its heavy midwinter garb, she felt as if she was seeing it in its true light for the first time. Gone were the silken shades of summer, soft veils of water across smooth sands, below a sapphire sky. Gone was the benign playfulness of summer breezes. Here was the Solway: bare, muscled and unadorned, and it made her shiver.

The already slim crew had been trimmed even further to a skeleton operation of twenty-four artists, crew, extras and the set security team who'd all been checked out for this final scene, which would appear somewhere in the middle of the completed movie. Shona saw they'd retained the extras from the earlier shoot on Hildan Island: Becca's friend, the slim teenager, the one-armed man, the fit-looking older woman with the long, undyed, white hair and the two skinny, balding men.

Shona reserved special scrutiny for Brian Aston, who, in full smuggler garb, hobbled across the rough ground, helped by one of the wardrobe girls. The Two Kirsties had reported back that he'd been courteous when they'd paid him a visit. He'd affected shock that his behaviour towards James McGowan's fans had been misinterpreted but accepted the officers' friendly advice to keep away from them in future. When he saw Shona watching, he gave her a wave. Shona glowered back, hoping to convey the distinct impression that if he was up to no good, then she was watching him.

The whole schedule was on the clock, as the fore-cast painted a picture of deteriorating weather for the short winter day ahead. Simon the director had everyone working at maximum efficiency. He walked between crew and extras, clapping his gloved hands together and urging them on like an invested uncle at a football match.

The scene depicted an attempt by Burns to capture the same smugglers who would later kidnap his friend John Syme as they hid their cargo by lanternlight in a cave. Becca was again adorned in long skirt and heavy cloak by the three costume and make-up girls who were battling to perform their role in a makeshift tent. Next to them, the father-and-daughter armoury team, Sven and Caris Wales, were preparing pistols and swords. Barry Perkins, the scriptwriter, looked thoroughly miserable, attempting to shelter the tablet he was using to make notes from the stinging sand, blown on a wind that harried him like a stray dog.

With Matt and the other staff from set security forming a cordon, Ric and Ben crossed to where Shona stood a little way back from the rocky shore, scanning the clifftops. The location, on private land, had been searched earlier this morning by estate staff with dogs. The tide was out, and they'd easily spot someone foolhardy enough to approach across the treacherous Solway sands.

But a sniper who'd somehow evaded the gamekeepers and was hidden in one of the bushes could be a real threat. Somehow, they needed to keep James literally out of the firing line. Shona was glad to see he was by the costume tent, taking Ric's advice to stay close to the cliffs and not wander out into full view.

'Don't like the look of this,' Ric said, eyeing the gaping mouth of the cave. It was a triangular cleft in the sea-blackened rock that rose ten metres high to a point, but inside widened out into a kind of hallway, thus allowing the crew sufficient room to work. 'How far d'you reckon it goes in?'

'The estate manager thought it had a dead end,' Shona replied. 'But he admitted some of these former smugglers' caves are notorious for having hidden entrances and exits.'

'Right, guess we better check it out.'

Ric and Ben donned headtorches and went in, their voices echoing off the rock. Five minutes later they returned.

'Couldn't find the end of it,' Ric said. 'We had to stop when it got a bit squeezy. Reckon we should block it off, just in case. Don't want any unexpected visitors.'

They collected a couple of long driftwood planks that lay on the tideline. Then they moved towards the old salmon fishing posts, jammed upright into the sands but abandoned for fifty years, their rotting remains stretching out like the bones of some long-dead leviathan. Ben took a knife from his pocket and began cutting free discarded netting that was tangled around them, before both men went back into the cave.

They soon returned, announcing they were as satisfied as they could be. Jan, the director of photography, signalled he was happy too. His assistant stood by with a portable LED light on a long boom, the colour adjusted to the warm lamplight glow that would bolster the oil lanterns of the smugglers.

The extras were brought down to the mouth of the cave for a final briefing from Simon. Shona noticed Becca listening intently to the director's words. James wanted to do a single take to retain the spontaneity of his performance, and with the freezing weather set to deteriorate, the tide-clock ticking and the ever-present threat from the stalker, no one on the beach argued with that. The armourer, Sven, after handing James his sword, walked over and joined the group, adding instructions of his own to the background actors.

James stood alone a little way off, in a protected spot where the cliff formed a shallow bay of rock, his greatcoat flapping, impervious to the cold, his back to the director and the crew, face to the Solway skies. He turned to Shona and extended his hand, beckoning her into the shelter. She joined him. With a shy, conspiratorial smile, he slowly drew the point of his sword across the smooth sand at her feet – J&S, enclosed by a heart – but quickly wiped it away before anyone else could spot it.

Shona felt a flood of warmth. Her hand went to her mouth, covering the wide smile that verged – she was embarrassed to note – on a giggle, and that she was convinced everyone else on the beach had noticed.

It was like they'd picked up where they'd left off outside the school disco. It felt pure and honest and so, so right.

What exactly did he want? For that matter, what did she want? She wasn't sure of anything other than a fierce, burning desire to protect this man from whatever evil was stalking him. If she could just keep him safe, she would eventually understand what thread had drawn them together after all these years and how tightly it bound them.

The sky darkened, and suddenly a squall of rain and wind swept in. But this was the Solway and, further up the coast, Shona glimpsed a sudden dazzling brightness that shone on the land like a snapshot of another time. Even in the depths of winter, there were green shoots and a flash of golden gorse.

Simon called for the take. James, with a last smile, turned and strode towards the others.

With James securely in the cave, Ric and Ben stationed themselves outside. No one could approach the set without being clocked. At the last minute, Shona joined the crew inside and slid behind the camera position. Out of the wind, the sudden silence seemed unnaturally loud, the air close and damp with the salt-tang tinge of rotting seaweed. The armourers handed James and the smuggler their pistols and repeated the warning to the extras crowded at the sides, some clutching sacks or wooden boxes of illicit booze, that the sound would be amplified by the enclosed nature of the cave.

'Quiet now, please,' Simon said.

Everyone stilled, ready for the director's word. In the dim light, their faces seemed carved from the rock itself, gargoyle representations of the real rumrunners and contrabandists who had once passed this way.

'And... action.'

The smugglers bustled towards the back of the cave, their lanterns carving orbs of light from the darkness which seemed to press in on them. Robert Burns appeared silhouetted against the cave mouth, a pistol in each hand.

'Surrender yersels in the name o' His Majesty's Excise.'

There were shouts and confusion as the smugglers attempted to flee, pushing each other and scrabbling over the uneven floor of the cave. On cue, Burns fired, and the booming reply of the smuggler's pistol answered.

Shona felt the noise pass through her chest like a solid object and swallowed to clear the pressure wave from her ears. Smoke filled the cave, billowing upwards in plumes that glowed in the sulphurous light. She saw figures stagger back, James among them.

'Cut!' Simon called.

The extras stood up, grinning and dusting the sand from their costumes, and Shona waited for James to follow. He needn't extend his habitation of Burns now, surely? Sven the armourer, having retrieved the smuggler's weapon, bent down to recover Burns's double-barrelled pistols. Even in the low light from the cave entrance, Shona saw his expression register shock.

She pushed through the extras, giddy with adrenaline, and fell to her knees next to James. His face was in shadow, turned away. She touched his cheek. His head lolled towards her, and she saw the bright bloom of blood across his temple.

'No, no, no,' she panted, pulling off her pashmina and pressing it to the wound. She leaned forward, listening for his breath. Her cheek brushed his. It was ice cold.

She'd failed and it was James McGowan who'd paid the price.

Chapter 30

Sven the armourer stood next to her, staring at the pistols in his hand as if he'd never seen them before. 'Impossible. No live ammunition on set. It was just flash powder.' He repeated this like a mantra, until Shona barked at him.

'Get Ric. And secure those weapons.'

The director hurried over, a look of confusion and horror on his face. 'Oh my God. What happened?'

'He's been shot.' Shona heard the tremor in her own voice. 'Get folk out of the cave, but no one leaves the set. Check if anyone else has been injured!' Shona called after Simon as he hurried away.

She was desperate for a glimpse of Becca to confirm she was okay, but dared not shift her focus from James, whose breaths were so shallow they were almost undetectable. His skin tone was growing greyer by the second.

Ric dropped beside her and felt for a pulse beneath James's jaw. Then he raised a thumbs up to Ben, already running backwards from the shadow of the cliff, searching for a signal, phone clamped to his ear. He returned the gesture, indicating he'd reached the ambulance control.

'First aid!' Ric roared.

When nobody moved, Becca – who was unharmed and had a comforting arm around her friend – ran to the costume tent, grabbed the red bag and brought it to the cave.

Ric took out his headtorch and turned it on, nodding to Shona, who eased back the pashmina to reveal a long bloody wound running from back to front above James's ear, and a flash of pale bone beneath his torn scalp. She clamped the pressure back on.

Ric felt across James's head. 'Don't think the bullet pierced the skull, but there's damage at the back. Must have hit a rock on the way down.'

Becca unzipped the first-aid pack. It didn't contain the kind of military grade haemostatic dressings needed to reduce bleeding in gunshot wounds. They'd have to improvise. Ric rummaged through the bag and handed her two gauze pads. Together they slid them beneath the scarf, Ric holding James's neck to stabilise it as Shona re-clamped the wounds, adding a wide crepe bandage around his head.

Focus. Just keep him alive. That was all she had to do. Just keep him alive.

'It's okay, Jaz,' she said. 'Paramedics are coming. We'll get you as comfortable as we can. Ric and Ben are on it. Becca's here too.'

At the sound of her voice, his eyelids flickered. She had no idea if he could hear her, but anything that anchored him to life was worth trying.

'Dove and Beau will be glad to see you. You need to hang on for them.'

And for me, she wanted to say: hang on for me because now that we've found each other again, I can't lose you, not like this.

'The coastguard helicopter won't be able to land here,' Shona said quickly to Ric. Even if the gusty wind moderated, the deceptive sands, more water than earth in places, would never bear the weight of the seven-ton helicopter.

Her other thought had been to call on the lifeboat to extract James, but the tide was too far out. 'We'll need to carry him to the road.'

While Shona monitored James, Ric disappeared into the darkness at the rear of the cave. Outside, Matt from set security had at least had the presence of mind to herd the extras and crew away from the cave and into a sheltered spot out of the wind.

Shona's ears roared from the pistol's retort, making her feel as if the tide was rushing in and would trap them in the cave. She fought the urge to look over her shoulder.

The shot had come from one of the set pistols. Flint-locks worked differently from modern guns. To load an antique weapon, powder had to be poured down the barrel, followed by a cloth wad and a lead ball, which was then tamped down. More gunpowder was added to an external pan. Pulling the trigger caused a spark from the flint to ignite the powder, and the resultant explosion propelled the lead ball out.

Most set weapons were replicas or decommissioned and had filled barrels, making it impossible for them to fire any projectile, but James, with his passion for authenticity, had insisted on genuine antique pieces.

Looking up, she could see Ben outside taking charge of the situation. The weapons were now safely locked in the gun chest, and the key was in his hand. All she had to do was keep James alive, but blood was soaking through the gauze pads, pooling dark and gritty in the sand beneath him.

She replaced the pashmina over the dressing.

'Becca.' She took her daughter's hand and positioned it over the scarf. 'Keep pressing firmly.'

She ripped open the last two packets of gauze pads, and without removing the first bandage, tied them tight with the bloodied pale blue pashmina, giving an almost jaunty aspect to James's Burns costume.

'Is he going to die?' Becca said, her eyes wide, still on her knees beside James.

'No,' Shona said firmly, as much to convince herself as Becca.

James stirred, his eyelids flickering.

Shona felt a rush of relief that he hadn't fallen so far into unconsciousness as she'd feared. 'Jaz, hang on. We're getting you out of here.'

He began to flail in panic. He clawed at the makeshift dressing. She grabbed his hands and pinned his upper body with her own.

'Stay still,' Shona said. 'Squeeze my hand. Dinnae let go.'

Ric reappeared with the driftwood spars they'd used to block the landward entrance of the cave and fashioned them into a battlefield stretcher.

He summoned his colleague with his customary sharp whistle and Ben ran into the cave.

Shona's face was close to James's, and she saw the slackening of the muscles around his mouth and eyes as he drifted away from her once more. 'Jaz, open your eyes, ma love.'

But there was no response. She could feel a rising panic gripping her throat, making her choke back tears as his bloodied fingers loosened from her own.

Even if he hadn't by some miracle fractured his skull, the twin impacts from bullet and rock had likely caused a traumatic brain injury. Without oxygen and medication to prevent clots forming, it would be fatal.

Ben took Shona by the shoulder and gently but firmly moved her aside.

'Becca, cloak,' Ric said.

Quickly, they cocooned James in coat and cloak, and strapped him onto the makeshift stretcher.

A line of shocked faces passed in a blur as Ric and Ben set off at a lick along the beach, with Shona stumbling behind them. She tried not to picture how they'd become so adept at handling a seriously wounded casualty on a stretcher, and the survival rate of their previous passengers. No wonder Lilly Chase valued Ricardo and Benji so highly. Her trust wasn't misplaced.

Shona knew she should stay at the scene, but she was convinced everyone there were witnesses, not suspects – the armourer's shock was genuine, she was sure – and she couldn't bear to leave James.

Shit. This was what the three bullets had meant. She'd been so wrapped up in the idea that the threat had been from Delfont. The warning had been plain, and she hadn't seen it. The stalker had been taunting them. The number was irrelevant. He'd planned to shoot James all along.

She knew ambulance control would have alerted CID when they'd received Ben's call, but as Shona ran behind, she took out her own phone, relieved to see she had a signal.

'Murdo!' she gasped when he picked up.

'Already on the way, boss,' he said over the noise of traffic and sirens.

They arrived at the field where the crew vehicles were parked just as the ambulance was waved through the gate by one of Matt's black-clad security men.

As Ric and Ben lowered James to the ground, Shona was torn between remaining by his side and directing the police operation. An officer's first priority is the preservation of life, and she knew what she must do. Shona ran up to the driver's door, fumbling for her warrant card.

'DI Shona Oliver,' she said. 'Gunshot wound to the head. Extensive blood loss. Casualty's been unresponsive for...' She checked her watch. '...twenty minutes.'

Ric cut James free from the stretcher and was rubbing his face, prising up an eyelid to check his pupils were still responding to light. 'Come on, mate. Come on.'

The paramedics ran forward and for a moment James himself seemed to disappear under foil blankets as the four men struggled to bring him back. She fought the urge to rush in, to cling to him as if by grasping his body, she could stop his life slipping away. Then she heard his muffled splutter as he was hauled back from the edge again. She stood rooted to the spot, her eyes fixed on his face, unable to look away.

The familiar sight of Murdo's car and Murdo himself, striding towards her in his suit and town shoes, brought her back to her senses. He grabbed her by the upper arms, and she realised she'd been swaying.

'Boss? You okay?'

She must have looked a sight. Her hands were caked in James's blood, which she realised was also smeared across her face.

'I'm fine, Murdo,' she replied, drawing in deep breaths. 'I'm not injured. It's just... James. Someone tampered with a pistol.'

He must have read something uncharacteristic in her expression, as he seemed to instinctively realise that, for Shona, James McGowan was not just another victim. 'D'you want to go in the ambulance?'

She absolutely did. But what about the scene? What about Becca?

'No, we'd better get down there. Set security have kept hold of everyone.' Just then, a second ambulance and two squad cars pulled into the field. 'Some folk might need treating for shock.'

Murdo gave her a look that said, *aye, and you're one o' them.*

She thought he might hug her. She prayed he wouldn't, because then she would break down completely. James was being loaded into the ambulance. Ben jumped in after him and she saw Ric jog to one of the fourbies. He pointed his index finger to indicate he was following.

Shona nodded. It was Ben and Ric's job to keep him safe. It was her job to find who had done this and stop them trying again. The rest was in the lap of the gods.

Chapter 31

Shona sent uniform and the paramedics over to the set and told them to seal it off, but anyone who needed treatment could be brought back to the vehicles where there were flasks of hot drinks, food and shelter. The others would follow once initial statements had been taken. With only twenty crew and extras, it shouldn't take more than an hour for Murdo and the four uniform officers to get through them.

But a bigger concern was the nature of the crime scene itself. The tide would reach the cave before SOCO did. The fact that they had the shooting on film was to their advantage, but any other forensic evidence would be swept away. Shona needed to talk to Sven the armourer urgently.

Murdo retrieved his wellingtons and a waterproof jacket from the boot of his car, and they set off back across the marsh. Halfway along the path, she crouched by a rock pool and washed the blood from her hands and face, knowing the effect it would have on witnesses. She tasted salt: suddenly, it seemed to her that the pool was a basin of her unshed tears. This is where she'd leave them, she told herself, safe in the Solway's care, until she'd caught whoever had tried to take James's life from him.

When they reached the set, crew and extras were split into two groups, half-sheltering inside the costume tent. The others – Simon the director, Jan and his assistant, the sound recordist, Barry the writer, and the father-and-daughter armourers – gathered nearby. Caris Wales was red-eyed and looked on the verge of collapse.

Becca broke away from the group and threw herself into her mother's arms.

'You're okay,' Shona said. 'He's alive. I need to deal with this first. Then we'll talk, okay?'

Becca nodded, mute with shock, as her mother smoothed back her hair, then crossed to the group gathered nearby.

Simon immediately asked how James was doing.

'He's alive, that's the main thing,' Shona said. 'The Royal is very good,' she assured them, suddenly feeling like she should stand up for their rural services. 'The paramedics, everyone… He'll get the best of care. Ric and Ben are with him. He'll be safe.' She turned to Sven and Caris. 'We need to talk.'

She and Murdo moved the armourers away to the nook where James had stood earlier and drawn the heart in the sand. The wind had edged round, and it was no longer the haven it had been. Shona saw again his smile, but it was overlaid by the image of him bleeding in the cave and she tried, with only partial success, to banish both from her thoughts.

Murdo formally cautioned the armourers.

'It's my fault,' Caris said, immediately. 'I had the smuggler's pistol. Dad primed the double-barrels.'

'We just need to establish the facts,' Shona said gently, then turned to Sven. 'It appears one of the pistols contained a projectile. Have you any idea how that could have happened?'

He shook his head vigorously. 'Impossible. We use flash powder not gunpowder. More light and noise, less

282

propulsion. Even if someone pushed an item into the barrel, there wouldn't be enough velocity. It's not like mistakenly putting a live bullet in a modern gun. This just couldn't happen. Not even by accident.'

As a firearms officer, Shona knew his technical assessment was correct: this was no accident.

'And the weapons are always secure, the gun chest kept locked, right up until you hand them to the actors?'

'Yes, even at the hotel and between takes.'

She'd observed the armourers operating on set. The fact that the antique weapons hadn't been decommissioned was a concern, but nothing she had seen had rung alarm bells or made her think they weren't sticking to protocols.

'I can't have checked the barrel was empty,' Caris cut in, shaking her head in self-reproach.

'You always do that? Even with antique guns?' Murdo asked.

'Always.'

'When?' Shona said.

'When we prime them with flash powder.'

'Anyone shown particular interest in the guns, who wouldn't normally have access?' Shona said.

'Everyone is interested in the weapons,' Sven said, wearily. 'Theft is a problem, so we're careful. The double-barrelled pistols alone are worth fifty grand.'

Murdo let out a low whistle.

'And actors always want to take their swords home as a souvenirs,' Sven continued. 'So we're eagle-eyed on that score. We watch every weapon on set, but I suppose it might just have been possible, in the dark of the cave, for someone to prime the pistol with gunpowder, insert a lead ball of the correct calibre, tamp it down. But you'd have to know what you were doing—'

'Or the gun might jam and misfire in your face,' Shona finished.

'Exactly,' Sven agreed.

'It's okay, Dad, you don't have to defend me,' Caris said with resignation. 'What will I be charged with?' She directed the question to Shona.

'Just concentrate on remembering what happened,' Shona said. Then she paused, calculating whether there was any possible link between the armourers and the Burns Supper incident. Explosives had been used then. But, motive aside, would Sven or Caris be stupid enough to use a method so easily traced back to them? They'd likely lose their licence and their livelihood over this. It didn't seem probable.

'Do you know who fired the shot?' Shona said.

There was only one primed pistol – other than James's – on the set today, which had been carried by a trained extra, whose whereabouts were already accounted for.

Sven pointed to one of the two balding smugglers. He sat on the sand with his back resting against the cliff and looked like he might be sick any minute.

'Gave his name as Harry Miller for the insurance,' Sven said.

Shona nodded to Murdo, who crossed to the man, encouraged him to his feet, cautioned him and sent him back to the car in the company of uniform. He and the armourers would be formally interviewed at the station, where they would make their statements and probably held for a minimum of twelve hours, while investigations were ongoing.

Shona checked her phone. A signal, but no update from Ric. She chewed her lip and assessed the tide. It would come fast but, without a visible warning line of white horses, just as an insidious creep that first filled the ridges in the sand, as if emerging from below, then accelerated faster than you could run. Already, pools were multiplying and growing like watery blooms. They were out of time.

'Right, Murdo,' she said when he returned. 'Get everyone off the beach.'

Shona crossed to the cave and told the two constables standing guard to make their way back to the carpark. The cordon tape was flapping faster in the strengthening breeze, as if panicked at the advancing weather and tide. She ducked beneath it, checking that all the movie equipment had been removed. With her phone, she took a couple of record shots to supplement those already gathered by the uniform constable that Murdo had tasked with the job. She forced herself to study the blood on the sand, the scrabbled tracks that she and the others had left as they'd fought to save James. She shone the light from her phone onto the rock behind where he'd stood. If the lead pistol ball hadn't entered his skull, then it must surely be in the cave somewhere, and on it might be a fingerprint, a trace of the killer's DNA.

But the wet rock played tricks on her. The light from her phone illuminated grey metallic gleam after gleam. Her hope was extinguished like a series of snuffed candles as she looked closer to find, not a pistol ball, but a fragment of seashell, a fleck of quartz or the empty husk of a barnacle clinging to the black wall.

A desperate voice in her head told her the evidence was here if only she looked hard enough. She began to swing her phone-torch around in wider arcs until she became disorientated, aware somehow of other voices, those of long-dead smugglers calling to her, as if they knew what she was looking for. They could show her. All she had to do was stay and keep looking. But when she turned towards the entrance to the cave, the light had changed. It was already growing dark. How long had she been inside? Minutes? Longer?

Someone was calling her name. Was it James? Had the violence witnessed by these rocks left some residual echo in the stone?

She stumbled out of the cave. The beach was gone. While her back was turned, the Solway had replaced it with a sheet of rippling water. Above sat the heavy grey mass of the storm front. Murdo stood by the end of the bay, shouting, his body language betraying his agitation. As she began picking her way along the remaining sliver of shore, she saw his lips move but the wind snatched the words away. In the sound of the waves, she heard their echo: *hurry, Shona, hurry*.

Chapter 32

The tide swept in, bringing with it fat, cold raindrops. Tent, boxes and kit were lugged back to the field whose previously frozen surface was becoming churned and hazardous. The remaining crew and extras stood by their vehicles, like the aftermath of a particularly unlucky bank holiday barbeque, desperate to leave but unsure if it was polite to do so.

Shona sent Murdo back to Cornwall Mount to begin collating the formal statements.

Her phone rang. Seeing Ric's name, she was torn between wanting and not wanting to know what he had to tell her. After taking a breath, she answered the call.

'Shona, love, he's alive. Needed plenty of blood. In fact, he's had more pints than a Scotsman on his stag night. But he'll make it.'

'Lasting damage?'

There was the briefest beat before Ric spoke again, all levity gone. 'Too early to say. They'll do scans later.'

Shona put her hand to her face. With a head injury like this, it was impossible to judge the long-term effects. Would he walk again? Remember his family, his children? Perhaps he wouldn't even recognise her?

'Thanks, Ric,' was all she managed to say. She was too drained to feel elation that James was still alive, but the sense of relief was so overwhelming that she thought her legs might go from under her.

'I can come and get you and Becca,' he offered. 'Ben's with him. I'm on my way over in a cab to pick up the other fourbie. I can take you back to High Pines if you like?'

Shona knew the conversation about her husband and his prison predicament that Ric had begun yesterday was sure to rear its ugly head. She didn't want to do that now. At least not until she'd spoken to Thalia. In any case, she was convinced the bullets had been sent by James's stalker. It was the most logical explanation, given recent events.

'It's fine,' Shona said. 'A squad car is taking us.'

Murdo had made it clear that he thought the boss should get some rest and could safely leave the current operation in his hands. There was nothing else she could do until forensics arrived at the cave at the next low water in six hours' time.

'And Ric,' Shona said, 'thank you for everything today. James was lucky. He probably owes you his life.'

'No worries,' Ric replied. 'He had you watching over him. I'd say that boy already has all the luck he needs. Cheerio.'

She felt the dig, but it wasn't uncomplimentary, and she was too relieved by Ric's news to worry about anything else he might say. She could choose to believe, if she wanted, that he was referring solely to her professional abilities.

Shona crossed to Becca. 'James is stable. We just need to wait.'

Becca hugged her mother. This time, Shona could do nothing to stop the tears welling in her eyes. She buried her face in her daughter's hair. The damp wool of her costume made her feel and smell unfamiliar.

'I like James,' Becca said.

'I like him too.'

'I know you do,' Becca replied, giving her mother a knowing look and hugging her tighter.

–

The fans were absent when the squad car drew up at High Pines. News of the shooting was all over the media. Shona wondered at the shock it must have delivered to Callie McGowan and the others, who viewed James as a close member of their family. It would hit everyone hard but probably not deter them from besieging Dumfries and Galloway Royal Infirmary for as long as he remained there.

Shona made Becca stay in the car while she and the two uniform officers checked the house. As James's survival was now being widely reported, his stalker, still on the loose, might feel there was nothing to lose by venting his frustration on those who'd supported the man he had – for whatever reason – targeted.

She still couldn't confidently say that the person responsible was the same man who'd grabbed Becca in the garden. But either way, she was taking no chances. She'd also advised everyone who'd been on the set – cast and crew – to be extra vigilant until James's stalker was caught and, after what they'd witnessed, nobody had argued.

When the house was declared clear, she took Becca inside, and thanked the uniform officers for their help, bolting the door after they left. She sent Becca upstairs for a hot shower, then went through the house, drawing the curtains and turning on the lights. Ric wasn't back yet and anxiety that Delfont or one of his associates might be out there, in addition to James's stalker, made the hairs on the back of her neck prickle. When she got to the floor lamp that James had fixed, she almost broke down, before reminding herself he was alive. She switched the lamp on and felt a little of his warmth flow into the room.

The gate buzzer sounded in the kitchen. Probably Ric, Shona thought. But on checking the security screen, she was surprised to see Tommy and Freya, collars up against the rain. The lights must have alerted them to her return, and she was touched that they'd come to check on her and Becca.

Freya put down the two foil-covered plates she was carrying in the utility room and hugged Shona, then held her at arm's length for assessment. The older woman's face was full of kindness, and she didn't ask Shona to recount what had happened.

'We're no' staying,' Freya said. 'I'll pop your dinners intae the oven. A couple of Moroccan chickpea tagines fur you and the lassie.'

'Thanks, Freya.' Shona smiled. 'You really didn't have to.'

'It's no problem.' Freya patted her hand. 'The Royal Arms can run to a couple of meals after all the business you've brought in wi' thon film folk.' She glanced at Tommy, who was shifting from foot to foot, hands plunged deep in the pockets of his jacket. 'Say yer piece and we'll be off and let the wummin get somethin' to eat.'

'Larry Smith…' Tommy began. 'I know where he is.'

Shona's attention flicked from Tommy to Freya and back. He saw Shona's look.

'It's fine. She knows,' he said.

Freya turned away and busied herself with the food preparation.

'I thought you might be tempted to go after him yourself,' Shona said.

'Aye, I was, but for once I thought better of it.'

Shona reckoned Freya had had a hand in that decision. She was thankful and relieved that his confession hadn't caused the rift between them that Tommy had predicted, but it still might take time for Freya to process his historic connection to smuggling.

'Smith's on a boat in Maryport Marina,' Tommy went on. 'A friend of mine saw him when he went o'er this mornin'. It's called *Kismet*. Think he's been living on it.'

Shona nodded. 'Thank you. You did the right thing telling me.' She paused to emphasise her point. 'The fiscal's already issued a warrant on the *Ranger*. Larry Smith is a person of interest. I can relay this, and that'll be the end of it, for you, I'm sure.'

Tommy looked relieved and although Freya had her back to him, her posture seemed to have softened too. When she turned around, she was smiling.

Once the couple had left, Shona called Dan Ridley in Cumbria. 'I've been meaning to get back to you,' he said, apologetically.

'It's fine. Listen…' She relayed Tommy's tip and told Dan to get down to Maryport Marina as soon as he could. Then she phoned Murdo and told him that Dan would let him know when Smith was in custody. Cumbria Police could hold Larry Smith until Murdo sent a car over.

'That's the last loose end,' Murdo said. 'At least with our bit of the smuggling chain. Trading Standards will be calling us with all their problems now.'

'Always glad to work with partner agencies,' Shona said.

'Oh, aye,' Murdo agreed. 'Team effort every time. And I'm sure we've no' seen the back o' smuggling, that's for sure. Burns knew it, and we know it, but maybe we've made the buggers think twice about trading on our patch.'

Becca came into the kitchen, pyjamas on and wet hair bundled up in a towel. She looked exhausted but perked up at the smell of Freya's cooking. Shona pointed to the oven.

'Listen, Murdo, I better go.' She felt suddenly as tired as Becca looked. 'Update me if anything happens. I'll meet you back at the beach at midnight.'

'Any news on when we might interview McGowan?' Murdo said.

Shona had received a text update from Ric on the drive home.

'Doctors reckon if he has a good night, they'll withdraw sedation tomorrow.'

'That's good.'

'Yes, Murdo, it is. See you later.'

Let him have a good night, Shona prayed, for all sorts of reasons.

Chapter 33

Just before midnight, Shona left Becca asleep, the walkie-talkie next to her bed. Ric and Ben were taking it in shifts to watch over James at the hospital, while one of them remained in the guest suite should Becca need them.

The squall had been intense but mercifully short-lived. Shona stepped outside and zipped up her fleece. The cold gnawed at her ears and fingers. A sparkle of frost, lit by the full moon, gleamed on the tarmac as she crossed to her car. They'd sold Rob's Volvo. The sole family car was now Shona's six-year-old Audi. Despite the lack of public transport, and the fact she'd be seventeen in the summer, Becca showed no desire to start driving lessons, citing environmental factors as the prime reason. Shona had to admit that a second licence in the family would be a bonus when it came to keeping the business afloat, even if it was just for supermarket runs up to Castle Douglas, taking a bust Hoover for repairs or dealing with last-minute special requests from the guests – all duties that fell solely in her lap. Would she be able to keep the business going after the film company left?

She felt a wave of guilt that she was even considering such problems while James McGowan was in hospital, and his attacker still at large. As she turned the key and the Audi coughed awake, she bundled such thoughts into the bulging mental box marked *later* and set off for Colvend.

In the makeshift field carpark, she pulled up next to the forensic van and saw it was occupied not by the apprentice of the previous Hildan Island visit, but the magician himself. Senior Crime Scene Examiner Peter Harrison was about Shona's age, with close-cropped, receding dark hair and the focused, deliberate movements of someone at home in any environment, which was just as well, given his career choice. It was unlikely that he'd been the on-call SOCO and had probably been hauled from his bed in Edinburgh by top brass. He had a reputation for extracting scientific evidence where others failed, and they'd need all of his dark arts to find anything in the tide-scoured cave of a crime scene.

'Appreciate you coming down,' Shona said, shaking his hand.

'I'd appreciate you not using my junior staff as a chew toy,' he replied, with a mischievous twinkle, referring to Shona's recent encounter with the newbie forensics officer on Hildan.

'He needed telling,' Shona said, without rancour.

'Fair enough,' Peter replied with a shrug, a smile still playing around his lips. 'Dealing with bolshy DIs is all part of the learning curve.'

'What an accusation, after I've brought you to this lovely beach for a midnight stroll.'

'Aye well, I don't mean to sound ungrateful, but shall we promenade before we all freeze to death?' As he pulled on his boots, Peter placed one hand on her shoulder, retaining his balance. 'Heard you witnessed the shooting. Try not to make a habit of it or folks will say you're drumming up your own business.' He gave her shoulder a squeeze. 'Even superheroes have the decency to wait for the bat-signal.'

'Believe me, Peter, after today I'd happily hang up my cloak.'

'Oh, I very much doubt that,' he said with a wink. He clapped his hands together and nodded to an approaching figure. 'Here's Murdo, so let's get on before the tide comes back in. I'd rather save the moonlit swim for another night.'

The marsh — sinister enough by day — had taken on an even more threatening hue by night. Shona felt the shadows press in, and the familiar path became narrower and strewn with fresh trip points, so it took almost twice as long to reach the beach as it had in daylight. The clank and heft of the modern scientific equipment they carried seemed insignificant talismans against what lurked beyond their vision. The knowledge that this would likely be a fruitless errand further dampened her mood. In her mind, she held a lantern — James was alive — but it felt like a pinprick in the gloom which concealed a foe who seemed to shift and change.

The cave appeared somehow bigger than it did in daylight, cut into the cliff like the stuff of nightmares: a featureless, gaping maw that struck at something primeval within them. Shona's footsteps faltered and she wondered if she'd been right to dismiss Murdo's offer to oversee the forensic recovery. The horror she'd witnessed earlier that day was feeding a deep desire to run. It was interfering with her decision-making in a way she'd rarely encountered. Even during the rescue of the conniving and duplicitous Larry Smith and his drifting yacht in the teeth of a gale, when there had been real danger they might both be swept overboard into the churning sea, she'd held fast. It was what she needed to do now. Hold fast.

She walked to the head of the group and found Peter, a literal white knight in his forensic overalls. The cordon tape had been breached and hung in a pair of ribbons from each side, as if some VIP had come on the tide to do the honours.

'There's flat sand for you to set up inside,' she said, making an effort to keep her voice calm. 'The victim fell to the left of the entrance. The shooter was potentially standing three or four metres towards the rear of the cave, but with the rock walls, a ricochet's also possible. The projectile may be a bullet, but more likely a lead musket ball.'

'Okay. Thanks, Shona.' Peter turned to his two assistants. 'Let's get started.'

Inside, the arc-lights were switched on and the cave sprang into view. It seemed to make the surrounding darkness bigger, banishing it outside where it lurked uncontained. On the floor, the bloodstains were gone, the sea having washed two metres up the wall at high tide. The same strong scent of rotting seaweed remained, sharpened by the cold and recent salt water.

'I'm just going to check the back,' Peter said. 'In case anything has been swept further into the cave.'

The walls crawled with scavenging, night-hunting crabs who scurried into the shadows. Shona shivered with the thought of what would happen to anyone who sought refuge from the advancing tide in here.

She jumped as Murdo touched her arm.

'Let's go outside, boss. Keep out of folks' way.'

Shona stood for a moment, letting her eyes adjust, then they moved a little way off from the cave mouth. The was no ambient light – not a house, nor a streetlight, and even the stars were faint beyond a veil of sea mist. The moon had fallen lower and was due to set at 2:27 a.m. when the ashen sands would become even darker. On the cliffs above, she heard animals moving about, the air so still that every sound was amplified.

Murdo cleared his throat. 'I'm very sorry about what happened wi' Rob. If there's anything Joan or I can do, just let me know.'

'Thanks, Murdo,' Shona said. Rob's stock had never been high with her sergeant, so she appreciated the offer.

''Cos it's no' right.'

'No.' She sighed. 'It's not.'

And Murdo, you don't know the half of it, she wanted to say.

'I didnae just mean the verdict. The gambling. The way he's treated you and your lassie. It's no' right. We're here to help if we can.'

In the dark, she couldn't gauge his expression. Perhaps he did know the half of it, or at least suspected. Murdo was a good cop, a thoroughly decent human being, and no pushover. Perhaps he'd even guessed the true depth of her relationship with James McGowan. It wouldn't have been hard. It was written all over her face when they'd loaded him into the ambulance. Surprisingly, she felt no guilt at the thought. Churchgoing Murdo had married his childhood sweetheart, and never to her knowledge looked at another woman, but she knew his offer of support was genuine and without judgement.

She reached out in the darkness and touched his arm. 'Thanks, Murdo.'

'Nae bother,' he said, stamping his feet to shake off the cold. Or perhaps he was indicating that the fleeting moment of intimacy was at an end, and she was his boss once more.

A shout went up from the cave and one of the constables raised a hand towards them. 'Ma'am. They've found something.'

Shona and Murdo hurried over. Perhaps the lead musket ball was easier to see with significant wattage. The white silhouetted figure of Peter Harrison stood in the cave entrance like some spectral merman. In his right hand he held up an evidence bag too big for a small projectile. As Shona moved closer, she and Murdo exchanged a glance. She pulled out her phone. The screen lit up, showing there was a signal.

'Ric, does Ben still have the key for the gun chest from the set?'

'Naw. Handed it over to that nice blonde DC of yours, Kate. Think he got her phone number in return. Did well out of that deal, if you ask me.'

Shona thanked him and hung up. Murdo was already walking a few steps away and ringing the CID office.

Shona looked at the bag. 'How long's it been in the water? You sure this isn't some smuggler's artefact?'

Peter shook his head. 'Wedged in a cleft in the rock, doubt it even got wet. Oiled, cleaned and recently fired. Still smell the gunpowder.'

Murdo returned and confirmed the gun chest contained its full complement. There was no doubt about it. There had been a second flintlock pistol in the cave. Now all Shona needed to work out was who had fired it.

–

When she and Murdo got back to Cornwall Mount, Shona was, for once, speechless. Although it was dark outside and the clock showed 3:30 a.m., the CID room looked like a normal weekday afternoon and contained a full complement of staff. She rubbed her gritty eyes, but the vision persisted.

'Folk wanted to help,' Murdo offered by way of explanation. 'I'll get you some coffee.' He crossed to where Hannah was filling mugs from a line of vacuum flasks.

'Boss,' Ravi said, hurrying over. 'You need to see this.'

He led her to where Vinny Visuals sat, a discreet stack of empty Red Bull cans lined up on the corner of his desk. Vinny himself betrayed no evidence of any stimulants and slouched back in his chair in his habitual pose: one ankle resting on his other knee, and navigating his keyboard with one hand, while the other propped up his chin. Even during daylight hours, Shona had a constant urge to shake her visual investigations officer and tell him to wake up and pay attention. Ravi did the necessary on this occasion, tapping Vinny on the shoulder to alert him to Shona's arrival.

'Boss,' Vinny said with customary economy, barely glancing from the screen.

'This is the enhanced footage the film company gave us from the cave. See?'

Ravi pointed to an image of the group of smugglers, his barely contained excitement a polar opposite to Vinny's apparent inertia. On the screen, a slow-motion flash appeared as the extra, Harry Miller, who played the smuggler, fired his flintlock pistol in response to Burns's arrival. Amber smoke filled the screen in jerky increments. Ravi turned expectantly. Shona shook her head.

'Vinny, pal... slower this time,' Ravi said.

The images scrolled again, almost rinsed of meaning by the subtraction of motion, but then Shona saw it. Brief, almost imperceptible, but it was there.

'Second flash,' she said. 'Someone standing behind Miller.'

They ran an extended clip backwards and forwards but, in the smoke and darkness, it was impossible to track everyone's movements. She had no doubt Vinny could do it, given time, but that was precisely what they didn't have.

'And Miller doesn't know who it was?'

'Nope. He remembers hearing a big bang to his right, but he thought it was the echo from his own pistol bouncing back off the cave wall. We're compiling a plan of where everyone was standing.' Ravi nodded to the whiteboard where Kate and Hannah were adding names to circles arranged in a rough plan of the cave. There was her own name. She'd been behind the camera position, concentrating on James, but also monitoring the cave entrance, looking away from the point where the shot had been fired.

Shona closed her eyes and pictured again the scene, mentally ticking off the other occupants, then checked her recollection with the scheme on the board. Something wasn't right.

Becca hadn't been at the edge of the group, but in the middle. She remembered hugging her daughter in the carpark as the ambulance left with James, the unfamiliar scent of her thick wool costume. When Becca had been a child, Shona could pick out her daughter's school pullover from lost property by smell alone. She suspected every mother could. Then she realised what it was she'd smelled in the carpark: not just damp wool, but the sulphurous whiff of gunpowder.

The clock said it was just before four a.m. Phone to her ear, she crossed to the whiteboard and, taking the marker from Hannah, rubbed out Becca's name with a finger and relabelled a circle in the middle, just behind the armed smuggler Harry Miller. Her daughter picked up after the first ring.

'Thought you'd be asleep,' Shona said.

'And you decided to check?' Becca's sarcasm had little of its usual bite and Shona realised she was primed for bad news. A four a.m. phone call rarely brings the good variety, which was something Becca had learned as the daughter of a police officer.

'It's fine. James is okay. I just need to ask you something. Wait, I'm gonna send you a picture.'

Shona snapped the board and forwarded it to Becca. 'I'm putting you on speaker.'

'Why? Who's there?'

'Just Ravi. And Murdo.'

People had stopped what they were doing, sensing a breakthrough might be imminent. They edged closer, a circle of expectant faces.

'And a couple of others,' Shona hurried on. 'Listen, I know you've already said this in your statement, but can you confirm who was standing near you during the scene? See the circles? We need to put names to them.'

Becca was silent for a moment. 'I know Rosie was definitely behind me, 'cos she was worried she might accidently scream at the noise. Ruin the scene, get told off.'

Kate put her thick pen against the circle marked with the girl's name, consulted her sheet and nodded. They ran through some further names, which tallied with the plan.

'Who was on your right when the gun went off?'

Becca was silent for longer this time. 'Brian the Beard,' she said, eventually.

Hannah pointed to the tagged circle that marked the stooped, white-bearded Brian Aston, which currently placed him further back from Becca.

'The plan,' Shona began, 'puts—'

'It's wrong. He was definitely next to me, 'cos he trod on my cloak. Nearly choked me.'

From the corner of her eye, Shona saw Murdo lift his desk phone. Brian Aston had given his camper van as his address, currently parked at a site near Dalbeattie.

Shona's heart was thumping as she picked her own phone up from the desk and held it to her ear again. 'Okay, darling. You did really well.'

'Come back for breakfast, Mum,' Becca said, suddenly sounding like the child she'd so recently been.

'I will,' Shona said. 'If I can.' She needed to change out of her jeans and fleece. There'd be a hospital visit and possibly a media statement. 'Try to get some rest. Stay inside. Buzz Ric or Ben if you're worried. Promise I'll be back soon.'

Shona ended the call and quickly looked across again to Murdo, whose face was grim. It told her that her fears were realised.

'Brian Aston's skipped. His camper van is gone. Got the site owner up to check. He last saw it at ten o'clock, when he turned in.'

Shona crossed to the whiteboard and rapped on it. 'Listen up, folks.' Heads turned as she wrote, then underlined the name on the board. 'Brian Aston. Number one priority. Find him.'

Chapter 34

When Shona got back home, she let Becca sleep on rather than wake her again. She dozed herself for an hour, then showered, dressed and grabbed her car keys. Superintendent Davies's name flashed up on her phone before she'd made it out into the parking area.

'This all is very unfortunate,' he said, as if he'd turned up at a bar to find his favourite beer was off. 'No chance it was an accident, and we can blame the film company for negligence?'

'None. It wasn't one of their weapons.'

It had been a smart move, on Brian Aston's part, to use a flintlock pistol. If he'd been spotted in the cave, no one would have been likely to challenge him, meaning that – for whatever twisted reasons of his own – he could bring James McGowan's Robert Burns to a satisfyingly authentic end, jam the pistol into the rock cleft and walk off the set without anyone being the wiser.

'At least James McGowan's still alive,' Shona said with more indignation than she'd intended. 'And we know who was behind the shooting.'

'But do we know why?' the Super countered.

She was finding the need to inject a positive spin into every conversation with her boss exceptionally trying. Any more of this and she'd have flashbacks to early teenage chats with Becca as to why it would be really, really nice for her to stay with her childless Uncle Sandy and Aunt Caroline in the school holidays, an exercise in fantasy over fact that had scarred them both.

'We need to catch him first. Work the why out later,' Shona said abruptly.

Outside, it was barely light. Ric and Ben were keeping their tag-team watch on James. One of the fourbies had already gone, and the other vehicle looked like it hadn't been sitting there long. The windscreen on the Audi was frozen solid.

Shona cursed and pulled open the boot of her car, searching for the de-icer, while still clutching her phone. Her fingers were cold and clumsy. The lack of sleep, and the fear that James could have a relapse in the night, meant she didn't feel as sharp as she would have liked this morning. The notion she might miss something significant, as she had with the bullets in the post, niggled at her, making her irritable.

All she needed was sufficient evidence to convince a jury of Brian Aston's guilt. It would be up to the psychiatrists to work out the rest.

'I'm sorry, sir, I'm on my way to see Mr McGowan at the hospital,' she said, shaking the de-icer can and spraying it on the windscreen. 'I will update you as soon as we have news.'

'We have a press conference scheduled for this afternoon,' Davies said. 'I'd really like to give them a result by then. It might deter any other questions.'

He meant questions about Rob.

Villains caught to a strict timetable, Shona thought. If it was that easy, everyone would be doing it. Instead, she said, 'Yes, sir. I'll certainly do my best.'

Once she hit the main road, Shona called the office for an update. Aston's contact details with the extras agency turned out to be false. Devon and Cornwall Police had been quick off the mark. His home address existed – a Georgian seafront building in Plymouth – but the groggy Brian Aston who answered the door was an eighty-four-year-old retired teacher, and he had no idea who might have stolen his identity. A description and index number for the camper van had been circulated, and Ravi and Vinny Visuals were trying to pick it up on ANPR cameras near Colvend, as well as on the main routes out of Dumfries and Galloway to England, Northern Ireland or Scotland's populous central belt, with its airports and major train connections. She told them to go draft a couple of Specials in to help and to go home for a few hours' sleep, but she knew they wouldn't. They wanted Brian Aston caught as much as she did.

–

James McGowan looked smaller and paler beneath the bedsheets. Relief flooded through Shona. His head was bandaged, a thick dressing on the left side above his ear, and a nasal cannula continued to boost his oxygen intake. When he spoke, it was slow and quiet.

His recovery would be slow, but doctors believed his prognosis was good. Shona had steeled herself not to betray any emotion beyond professional concern and James helped by referring to her as *DI Oliver*. Not Shona, and certainly not *ma wee darlin'*.

She let Murdo lead the questioning, content to drink in James's solidity, his smell, his alive-ness. The pale skin inside his forearm, the curve of his ear, the tiny scar above his left eyebrow he'd got falling off a swing in a concrete Garthamlock playground as a child – feature by feature, the image of him injured on the sand dissipated, until she accepted that he had survived.

'And you never met the man calling hisself Brian Aston, before?' Murdo said.

James, propped up on three pillows, rolled his head a fraction from side to side.

'No. Never paid any heed to him on the set. Didnae speak to me.'

'And his picture doesnae put you in mind of anyone?' Murdo held up his phone with the photograph supplied by the extras agency, Aston looking much as he had in costume. 'Could he be a fan that's approached you previously? Maybe you had an altercation?'

They'd been through the notion of an irate fan after the Burns Supper, but it was important to revisit possible motives and experiences, as it had the potential to shake loose a memory lurking, forgotten and neglected, at the back of a victim's mind.

James narrowed his eyes, considering. 'Most of ma fans are lassies.' He shifted on the bed to look at Shona and she felt her stomach tighten under the intimacy of his gaze. 'You remember this guy?'

'I first saw him on the island, talking to Becca,' Shona confirmed. 'And I think he made a point of speaking to me at Hildan House. Perhaps because he knew I was a police officer.' She decided to skip the theory she and Kate had discussed, about Aston targeting James's fans, since no one had yet made a formal complaint.

'Do we need to re-interview Becca?' Murdo said.

'Everything she knows is in the statement,' Shona replied. Her daughter was generally astute at picking up on people's behaviour, but she hadn't spotted any red flags. 'She said he was like all the other professional background artists, but it's interesting none of the others had met him before.'

'If he wasnae an actor, he'd have stuck out,' James confirmed, his breathing laboured.

'What is it?' Murdo asked, noting her thoughtfulness.

'He talked about travelling back in time,' she added. '*All of them unlived futures.* What d'you suppose he meant by that?'

'Regrets a past decision?' Murdo said, frowning. 'Life no' going as planned.'

Shona nodded. 'The therapist I called mentioned that some stalkers are motivated by an attitude of entitlement. Perhaps he thinks you denied him an opportunity?' She looked at James enquiringly. When he shook his head, she turned to Murdo. 'I think we need to look at Red Sun Productions again, the company that folded after James withdrew from a project. Can you get me a full list of the investors, please?'

'Sure, boss.'

'Was never gonnae happen,' James protested. 'Agent handled that.'

'The therapist also said he may believe he's been humiliated, even with very little contact, and react in a vindictive way designed to cause distress and maximum damage to his victim's reputation.'

'So, could be someone I've no' actually met before?' James said, wearily.

She had to admit it was possible. If that was the case, it would make it much more difficult to confirm the stalker's identity and track where he might go now.

Shona's phone rang. Kate. She declined the call. A nurse, who reminded Shona of Freya in her bustling efficiency, came in with severe looks for the two detectives. She had a point: James appeared shattered. He'd pulled the sheet and light blanket up awkwardly over his chest like a child signalling he wanted to sleep.

'I need a minute with DI Oliver,' he breathed, turning apologetic eyes to Murdo, who got up from his chair with a nod. After a few medical checks, the nurse left too.

James slid his arm from beneath the sheet and held it out to Shona. 'Just for a wee minute,' he said.

She took his hand, and he drew hers against his chest. She felt the pulsing of his heart beneath her palm.

'Only beating 'cos of you,' he said.

Shona glanced towards the door, then leaned forward and softly kissed him.

'Ae fond kiss,' he murmured, and smiled, his eyes closing.

They were still for a moment, words unnecessary, fingers entwined until his breath became calm and even. Shona's phone buzzed again.

'To keep you safe, I need to take this,' she said quietly. James barely nodded, but gently uncurled his fingers, releasing her hand.

Shona slipped from the room. She heard the excitement in Kate's voice as soon as she answered.

'Forensics have a result on the IED. Latent print. There's a match.'

'Yes! And?' Shona said, impatiently.

'A Joseph Bishop, registered at an address in Falmouth. Done for fraud twenty years back. No further convictions. Cornish Police are on their way.'

Shona frowned. She'd not seen that name anywhere in the case notes. What was the link to Cornwall?

'Kate, since we know Aston's details are false, could Joseph Bishop be his real identity?'

She'd thought Brian Aston had been putting the accent on for effect, since Cornwall was synonymous with smugglers from Long John Silver to Poldark. How did someone from that area connect to James McGowan?

'If we believe it's the same person who shot McGowan and planted the bomb.'

'Callie Rivers McGowan said Brian Aston was outside the hotel with the fans on the night of the Burns Supper.'

'Well, if you'd gone to all that trouble, you'd want to see your handiwork, wouldn't you?' Kate said, dryly.

'Okay, thanks, Kate. Can you check if any of McGowan's movies were filmed in the area?'

'I wondered that, boss. Drew a blank. Oh, and boss? I don't suppose it matters now, but Callie just called me to say that Brian Aston, after telling her what a big fan of McGowan he was, did try to persuade her to engage in sexual activity. When she refused, Aston began badmouthing McGowan, saying how he was a talentless actor and he could tell her what he was really like.'

'I think Callie had a very lucky escape,' Shona said. 'I did wonder if his pursuit of James's fans was somehow part of his vendetta against him. Okay, Murdo and I will be back shortly, but update me as soon as you hear from Devon and Cornwall police.'

Murdo was talking to Ric in the corridor. Shona couldn't help but smile to herself as she noticed her sergeant stand straighter and pull his stomach in. She could swear the two nearby uniform officers were doing the same.

She wanted to stay, to sit outside James's room as Sonya Nicolson had done with her husband, believing her proximity helped the unconscious Sean. But Shona didn't have that luxury. She saw Ric give her a meaningful look. In that glance, a bargain was struck. He'd protect James. She'd find Brian Aston or Joseph Bishop, or whoever was behind the shooting. And they trusted each other to do just that.

Chapter 35

When Shona reached the CID office, it felt like a home-coming just climbing the stairs. After returning from the cave earlier, she'd barely been able to enter her own office. Now, Shona went straight in, dumped her bag on the floor and hung her suit jacket on the back of her chair.

DI Dalrymple had left her desk pretty much as he'd found it. The only difference had been the silver-framed picture of her with Rob and Becca, which now sat on a filing cabinet.

Her family. Before it had all gone wrong. Becca was the same height as Shona, aged ten or eleven. Rob's hair had silvered in his early thirties, which meant he looked much as he did now. The photo had been taken at a party in the back garden of their house in Camden, and she'd always treasured it. She had no photographs of her parents, only her school pictures and a couple with her gran, but no other images of her past.

She reached out to replace the framed picture in its customary position but stopped short. Was she clinging to what no longer existed? Something had shifted in her view of the world, but she could only glimpse it, as if through fog, and she had the sense that the more she pursued it, the more it would flee.

Murdo tapped her door, bringing her attention back to matters in hand.

'Here's the list of the Red Sun Productions company investors, boss.'

Shona scanned down the list of twenty names, and was surprised to see James's ex-agent, Bryson Drake, as the majority shareholder, with James himself having a 1 per cent stake. He hadn't seemed bothered by the company's collapse. Perhaps Hollywood was all about 'insider trading' – who you knew, not what you knew – between parties who hedged their investments across production companies and movies, knowing not all would succeed.

'Oh, and Dan's been on,' Murdo said with evident satisfaction. 'They've got our fake iPad smuggler, Larry Smith.'

'Excellent. D'you want to give DI Dalrymple the news?' Shona said, keen to play down her own role and any possible connection to Tommy McCall.

'Aye, if you think I should,' he said uncertainly.

Shona realised with a flush of pleasure that his world had been righted by her return and the feeling was mutual.

'Maybe a quick email to tie things up?' she suggested. 'Wouldn't do any harm to burnish Dan Ridley's star either.'

'Aye, I will,' Murdo said, glad as always to be doing a junior officer a good turn.

Kate, mobile phone to one ear, stuck her head round the door. *Cornwall*, she mouthed, and made a cutting motion with her hand across her throat. John Bishop, whose latent fingerprint had been recovered from the IED, wasn't at the address in Falmouth.

'Okay, thanks,' Kate said, hanging up. 'He's not been there for twenty years, apparently. Just disappeared. They're running a check and promised to get back to me.'

As Kate returned to her desk, Shona pulled up the report on the IED, and ran once more through its method of construction and the likely materials used. She scrolled to the end and stopped, her mind drifting to James of its own accord, as it so often did these days. Her attention rested on the ringless third finger of her left hand and she noted with mild surprise how quickly the pale line left by her wedding band had faded. She remembered her fingers tracing across James's body and smiled to herself. There was no doubt about it, the millions of women who admired those muscles on screen weren't wrong. Her wedding band was still tucked in her purse, untroubled, she was also surprised to find, by any notion of guilt. Then it struck her.

Gold.

The answer was gold.

Ravi tapped her door, carrying his laptop.

'Brian Aston… any luck?' Shona asked, her attention only half on her constable and his worried look.

'Think we've been following the wrong camper van,' Ravi said, with a sigh. 'Guy at the site must've got mixed up.'

'You've got to be kidding me! How could that have happened?'

'We double checked with the campsite owner's records. He's adamant he got it right, but there's no CCTV at the site and he just writes the registration plates down in a paper diary. He must have mixed up his customers, so of course we were looking for the wrong vehicle. Cairnryan Border Force cops have just stopped the van, and its driver's a Canadian tourist named Brent Douglas. Sorry, boss. We're going through all the other index numbers, but it'll take time.'

Ravi looked exhausted and she hadn't the heart to bollock him, knowing he had pulled a double or possibly a triple shift.

'We're sure this isn't our guy?' Shona said.

'He's fit, forties, blonde and six-foot-two, about as un-Brian-like as you can get.' Ravi turned his screen to show the emailed scan of Brent Douglas's Canadian passport.

Shona stared at the photo. Ravi was right. He was as un-Brian-like as you could get. But there was something, around the eyes, maybe, that tugged at her memory. She ran her hands across her face, rubbing at the tiredness that blurred her vision and conjured up ghosts. Perhaps it was the thought that Superintendent Davies was breathing down her neck or her desperation to protect James that made her look again at the lean, tanned and open face in the photograph. *If he wasnae an actor, he'd have stuck out* was what James had said. And Brian Aston hadn't stuck out at all. She thought of the mercurial way James and even the extras were able to change themselves, almost in an instant, and become unrecognisable. What would Brian Aston look like without the beard? Different hair?

'Shall I tell the ferry cops to let him go?' Ravi said.

'No,' she said. 'Get a team from Galloway to bring him over. Go to DI Dalrymple direct if you need to. Douglas's van was at the campsite. Maybe they had a conversation and Aston let something slip. This Brent Douglas is a witness if nothing else. Bring him in.'

–

Three hours later, in an interview room of Loreburn Street police office, with Ravi by her side, Shona sat across the table from Brent Douglas, thinking that sometimes, you just had to play your hunches.

She'd gone through the evidence – photos, IED report, PNC records – and now, she was sure. The tourist didn't seem fazed at the interruption to his holiday. He'd waived his right to a lawyer and now sat back in his chair, legs crossed, with even a faint smile playing about his lips. Shona wanted to reach across and wipe it from his face, like the make-up and prosthetics he'd so skilfully applied in order to fool cast, crew, herself and, most importantly, his former star client James McGowan.

She laid three photographs face up on the table, like playing cards in find-the-lady, except in this version, it was a man – and she'd already pegged him.

'Brian Aston, talented extra. Brent Douglas, tourist. Bryson Drake, Hollywood agent.' She pointed to each picture in turn. 'I'm sure DNA and fingerprints will confirm it, but in the meantime, let me congratulate you on your many convincing performances.'

He didn't reply, but the smile deepened. A tilt of his head acknowledged her praise as if it was his due.

Part of her wanted to throttle him there and then for what he'd done to James, but she didn't need to. If she was right, he'd hang himself in his desire for recognition.

'I've only one question, Bryson... or should I call you Joseph Bishop, the Falmouth fraudster?'

Bryson grimaced. 'Joseph Bishop was a role I left behind a long time ago.' His voice was strong, rich and distinctive, and without a Canadian or any other noticeable accent. 'But I think I can guess your question, DI Oliver. What was my motivation? What's anyone's motivation? Money and power, of course.'

'This is about the collapse of Red Sun, isn't it? The production company linked to the Robert the Bruce film that James pulled out of? You wanted him to focus on big money-making franchises, so you'd maximise your cut.'

'He'd have been much better going with my project than this Burns nonsense.'

'Do you know what gave you away, Bryson?' Shona said.

'Everyone is a critic.'

'It was the gold mine you worked in,' Shona said. 'The IED was constructed with material used for blasting. You were determined to outshine the star who left you. And not just kill him. You wanted to destroy everything he'd built, starting with his reputation.'

Shona could feel a righteous anger elbowing aside her resolve to flatter Bryson Drake into a detailed confession that couldn't be prised apart later in court. Next to her, Ravi picked up his pen and began tapping it on his notebook, a nervous habit triggered, Shona knew, by her tone and increasingly aggressive posture. But she didn't care. They already had enough evidence to build a case.

'James said you'd fancied yourself as an actor, but didn't make the grade.' It wasn't strictly what he'd said, but anger made her vindictive. 'Did it feel good to stand so close to your biggest star client and he didn't even recognise you? What a rush that must have been, fooling yourself that your acting powers were the greater.'

Not a flicker of emotion crossed his face to confirm or deny his motives. He had plenty of acting skill, she'd give him that.

She remembered the London postmark on the envelope containing the bullets.

'Perhaps you even flew down on the same plane that James had travelled on for Michael Vincent's funeral. We'll be checking the CCTV. And' – Shona stabbed the tabletop with her finger – 'coming into my garden, threatening my daughter – what gives you the right to do that?' She ploughed on. 'But the Burns Supper stunt. A wee bit overdramatic, don't you think?'

'Look,' said Bryson, his eyes firing up with hatred. 'I made that little Glasgow chancer wealthy and a star, and now the ungrateful little shit was walking away. I put everything I had behind him and Red Sun. He torpedoed it for some vanity project. He destroyed any chance I had for future financial security and creative fulfilment.'

'That's what's behind all this? Envy? Where did you get the idea you owned him? Is that why you targeted his fans? Did you enjoy those women debasing themselves in the vain hope of getting closer to James?' She saw him flinch as a fleck of her spittle landed on his cheek. 'Or was it just info gathering? Face it. You think you have power, but even his lowliest fans know James better than you do, because they love him. I—'

She stopped, aware Ravi's pen percussion had reached a crescendo and he was shifting uncomfortably in his seat.

Bryson uncrossed his legs and leaned forward on the table, holding Shona's gaze.

'I've watched you on the set, Shona. My advice is you should think long and hard before getting any more entangled with James McGowan than you already are.'

He was attempting to threaten or shame her – a married police officer dallying with a movie star who was also the victim in her case. Perhaps he'd get some legal traction out of it, but it was so pathetic that she almost laughed.

'Interview terminated.' She checked her watch. 'At 2:55 p.m.'

Ravi switched off the recorder. They were in plenty of time for the superintendent's press conference; that should keep him happy.

She turned to Ravi. 'DC Sarwar, take this man and charge him.'

She got up and, with the recorder switched off, leaned across the desk to Bryson Drake. His polished demeanour slipped, and she saw a flash of uncertainty in his eyes.

'Bigger bollocks than you have tried to frighten me and failed. My advice to *you* is get yourself a lawyer, 'cos you'll no' be topping up that tan anytime soon.'

Chapter 36

Shona was able to deliver the good news to James, hugging him with relief, not caring that Ric, Ben and three members of the nursing staff were in the room. Shona then went downstairs to the hospital entrance and found Callie McGowan among the fans. It was her statement that had, ultimately, put Shona on the right track. James would be thanking her in person, with tea at the London Ritz, just as soon as he was well enough. The envious glances of the other fans exceeded Callie's wildest dreams.

On the way home, Dan had called her from Maryport to say that more fake iPads had been found concealed on *Kismet*, and that Larry Smith was singing like a canary, just as Shona had predicted. However, Dan had found nothing in their police log involving the Derwentwater house she was interested in, or anything to connect Chief Inspector Harry Delfont to its ownership, but he planned to go over as soon as he was able to door-knock the neighbours. It was pretty remote. He wasn't hopeful. She thanked him and told him she'd appreciate it, but to be careful.

When Shona returned to High Pines that evening, she gathered up Rob's documents and stacked them in the boxes, retaining only the material from Katherine Jones showing Rob's absences. She'd forward what she'd found to his barrister, Anoushka, and let her talk to Rob about whether the appeal should go ahead. She'd done what she could. It was up to him now.

She added notes on the links that Thalia had uncovered between Delfont and the company that owned the Lake District house. Thalia's phone was still switched off. It worried Shona, but with no attacks or suicides reported on someone matching Thalia's description, perhaps her friend had simply decided to walk away from it all and get on with her life. Shona wouldn't blame her, but she had hoped that Thalia could at least talk to her about it. Next week, she'd arrange a meeting with the head of Operation Vita and take Anoushka with her. If they couldn't persuade him to put pressure on the Crown Prosecution Service to reopen the case against Delfont, Shona would go to the press.

After they'd eaten, Becca went upstairs to watch a movie with Ric, who, it transpired, had three teenage daughters with his American wife and was an unlikely fan of *Legally Blonde*.

In addition to the hospital's own security team, a single police officer remained outside James McGowan's room, to prevent any fan incursions, leaving Ben free to don a suit and, Shona suspected, head into Dumfries for a discreet rendezvous with DC Kate Irving. Shona was in the utility, loading the dishwasher, when her phone vibrated on the countertop, displaying an unknown number.

'Shona, it's me.' Thalia's voice was hushed, yet she sounded as if she was outdoors.

'Thalia, thank God. I've been really worried. Are you okay?'

There was a pause, then the words came out in a rush. 'I have to do it. I have to see that bastard face to face, so he knows what he's done to me. To all of us.'

'Wait. Slow down. Where are you?'

'I just wanted to say thank you, Shona, for all you tried to do.'

There was a finality in Thalia's tone that made Shona's blood turn to ice.

'Wait, Thalia. We need to talk. This new evidence in Rob's case… He wasn't even in the office when some of the transactions took place. If we connect Delfont to the house… it's a possible destination for the laundered funds. We prove that, and we'll be able to show that Rob was targeted to cover up Delfont's wrongdoing. That we all were.'

'It won't be enough, Shona.'

The line went dead, and Shona immediately redialled but Thalia didn't pick up.

There was only one place where Thalia could be going – the Derwentwater house. Shona had already located it on the map before she'd called Dan Ridley and asked him to check it out. It would take Shona a couple of hours to get there by car. She had to stop Thalia. At best, it might dash any hope of reigniting the case, with Delfont turning the tables to present himself as the victim of harassment. At worst, Thalia, on sick leave, would lose her job, and her already fragile mental health would plummet beyond recovery. For what? Giving him the chance to laugh in her face?

'Dan,' she said when he picked up. 'Are you still in Whitehaven?'

'Yeah. Why?'

Kirkness to Derwentwater was at least two hours by car, but England was only fifteen miles by sea across the Solway. She could be there in well under an hour.

'Wait for me.'

–

Shona stood on the foredeck of the *Silver Crest* as Tommy McCall guided it into Maryport harbour. He hadn't asked why she needed his help. Becca had just nodded, eyes on the TV, when Shona said she was popping out for a couple of hours. Ric had given her more of an interrogating look, but then obviously decided that, with McGowan's safety assured, whatever else she was up to wasn't any concern of his.

As she went to step ashore, Tommy held out a pay-as-you-go mobile. 'Turn your phone off, or better still, leave it with me.'

She looked at him in surprise. What did she have to hide? But if Delfont did decide to claim harassment, it might be better if her phone couldn't be fixed to a mast in his area. Thalia had obviously thought the same. Perhaps smugglers' tricks were legitimate when it came to self-protection.

The *Kismet* was easy to spot, moored on the far side of the marina, illuminated by the forensic team's lights. Dan's dark grey SEAT Leon was parked just behind it, visible in the reflected glow. She spotted him standing on the quayside, with his hands buried in the pockets of his dark bomber jacket. Beyond, the town lay in winter darkness.

When he saw her coming, he moved from the patch of light towards her. She told Dan what she suspected. Thalia was about to confront Delfont. It was a decision that would go badly for her and any future court case. Even if Dan could find Thalia, she'd be unlikely to listen, but knowing the area as he did, could he take her? Together she was sure they could talk her out of it.

He nodded, not questioning her logic. 'Let's go.'

Dan drove skilfully through the narrow Lake District lanes at high speed, hedges flying past in the headlights. Twenty minutes later they slowed. He squinted through the wet windscreen, checking the black-and-white fingerpost.

'It's up this way.' He turned right along a narrowing lane that hugged the water's edge until they came to a cattle grid that marked the start of the private road leading to the house. Dan pulled up and turned off his headlights. There was no sign of any other vehicle, but it was possible that Thalia had just driven straight up to the house or concealed a car nearby. Shona tried her phone again. It rang, but there was no answer. It was also possible she'd had second thoughts, and the last thing Shona wanted now was to be found wandering around Delfont's property, searching for Thalia Brookes, who might be tucked up in a pub ten miles away, drowning her sorrows. His security would be good, with cameras and probably a dog.

Shona wound down the window and listened, her eyes adjusting to the dark. The rain had stopped, and the clouds rolled away. There was only the faintest sound of wind. She and Dan sat without speaking, only the ticking of the cooling engine for company. To her left, the surface of Derwentwater itself was visible, pewter-smooth in the moonlight. Up ahead, the orange oblong of a lit window appeared to hang among the bare branches of the winter trees. The house was an ultra-modern, two-storey lodge with glass on three sides to take advantage of its lakeside position. A deck ran along the front, jutting out over the water, and a further, smaller building to one side appeared to be a boathouse.

Shona reached up and clicked off the courtesy light, then opened the door a fraction.

'I'm coming with you,' Dan whispered, pulling on his own door handle.

'Better if you stay here,' she said. 'Sounds quiet. I'll just walk up the drive for a quick look. If she is inside, I might see her through those massive windows. If I don't, we'll keep calling her phone until she answers. If she comes past you, just stop her and ring me.'

Shona stepped out into the cool scent of damp earth and pine. She carefully edged across the cattle grid and made her way slowly up the gravelled track, alert for the sound of a dog or the red wink of a security camera.

She was almost at the house when she heard a muffled voice – *get on your knees.*

Shona stopped in her tracks, listening. Against the background whisper of the wind came three faint pops, like bubbles bursting, then a splash. The water at the edge of the house was hidden by bushes, but a series of telltale platinum lines radiated out onto the smooth surface of the lake.

Before she could react, a shape loomed out of the darkness and hit her full pelt. Shona tumbled backwards. The impact knocked the breath from her. Grabbing at his waterproof jacket and kicking out, she attempted to throw the man off. Sharp stones on the track bit into her back and scalp.

Then she realised two things simultaneously. It wasn't a man attacking her, but a woman. And that woman was Thalia.

'Thalia, stop!' she gasped. 'It's me, Shona.'

The figure froze, allowing Shona to push her over onto the ground and get quickly to her feet. She leaned forward, panting, elbows on knees as Thalia slowly got up, all energy suddenly spent.

'Are you okay?' Shona said, panting. She took her friend's arm. 'Where's Delfont?'

Thalia slid from Shona's grip and backed away. Then she said calmly, 'He's in the water.'

'What? What have you done? Show me,' Shona ordered, but Thalia didn't move. 'Where's his wife? Is there anyone else here?'

'No,' Thalia replied.

'Come on.' Shona caught hold of Thalia's jacket and this time she allowed herself to be pulled up the short drive. Light was spilling from the house through an open door, onto the deck. Shona saw that Thalia was wearing a black waterproof jacket, trousers and beanie, and carrying a small rucksack. The illumination falling on her seemed to rouse her from her silence.

'You shouldn't have come. We need to get away.' She seemed to be staring at a point on the edge of the deck, as if expecting something to rise from the water.

Shona followed the line of her gaze then ran towards where Delfont must have gone in. The current wouldn't have taken him far. She lay down on the deck. When she plunged her arm in, the water held her in an icy grip. Then, she brushed against something and had to fight the urge to yank her hand away from whatever lurked beneath. Her fingers closed on fabric, the small buttons of a shirt biting into her flesh.

'Help me,' she called to Thalia as she struggled to drag Delfont out from between the wooden uprights, but the woman was rooted to the spot, eyes wide and staring. 'What have you done, Thalia?'

With a final tug, Delfont came free. He floated out from beneath the deck and suddenly his face loomed up towards Shona. She started back, stifling a cry of horror. Now, after all this time, she was face to face with the man who'd drugged and raped her, who'd put her husband in jail and threated her daughter. Bitter bile rose up into her mouth and she gagged, but her fingers remained gripped to his chest. She forced herself to look for signs of life, pulling his face clear of the water. Shona had known people survive in cold water for half an hour and it had barely been five minutes since she'd heard the splash. There was the bull-like head, and his hair, whiter than she remembered it, was floating out like a wreath against the dark water. The eyes were open, and he still seemed to hold the same mocking look, the bulbous lips in a sanctimonious smile. Then she saw them: three perfect dark circles on his temple, like marks made by the blunt end of a pencil. And she knew exactly what Thalia had done.

Chapter 37

One week later

Shona stopped on the beach in front of High Pines. Becca walked ahead of her, both glad to have a break from preparing the guest rooms for the new arrivals. Ric and Ben had gone back to LA, the Boat Hoose crew had departed, but the publicity surrounding the film had already created a buzz in the area and bookings for the summer were coming at a steady pace.

Shona watched her daughter bend to collect any curious stones that caught her eye. It seemed to Shona that the pebbles on this shore were exceptional in their size, variety and colour. Some were round like gulls' eggs, their surface a smooth and speckled blue-green. Others were long, polished globules of shining jet. There were plates of slate so perfect in their geometry that it was hard to believe they hadn't been cut by machine. Even the grey pebbles had concentric hoops of silver quartz pulsing through them. Others were marked by streaks of rusty brown like spent blood. It was a testament to the Solway's power and reach that it could hoard such treasures for itself, piling them up on its shores.

Thalia had stayed for a day at High Pines before leaving to resume her walking holiday along Hadrian's Wall, which they'd agreed was her reason for being in Cumbria, should anyone ask. Shona drove her to Bowness-on-Solway at the wall's western end and hugged her goodbye.

The previous night, her friend had seemed frozen with shock as Shona had hurried her back to Dan's car. Dan's concern at the time had been for Thalia's and Shona's wellbeing. As they returned to Maryport, she'd told him nothing of the events that had unfolded at the house, letting him believe she'd found Thalia distressed on the driveway, and leaving him to piece together a possible alternative narrative later. As the *Silver Crest* crossed the firth, Shona had seen Thalia drop something into the sea. The three small-calibre bullet holes in Delfont's skull – one for each of his known victims – had told their own story.

Delfont's body had washed up two days later on the shores of Derwentwater. He'd been alone in the house, as his wife had gone to visit her mother in Birmingham. Police investigations established he had indeed owned the property, purchased with funds of unknown origin: they were working on the basis that the detective chief inspector had been the victim of a gangland hit.

Shona felt no remorse at Delfont's death, only regret that he wouldn't now face official justice and a lengthy prison term. Her guilt was reserved for Dan and Tommy. In her bid to save Thalia, she'd unwittingly put Dan's career, and perhaps his freedom, in jeopardy. Having just helped Tommy escape the mental chains of his smuggling past and persuaded him not to go after Larry Smith himself, she'd potentially landed him in an even worse situation – accessory to a murder.

She could tell Thalia to turn herself in, but where would that leave Shona?

By her actions, Thalia had created natural justice for Delfont's victims. But Shona had realised that there was something more important to her than justice – her family. Delfont was no longer a threat to Becca, or Rob, or to her. Her daughter's life would be infinitely better with Delfont dead, and that was what mattered most.

It had been easy for Delfont's cronies to put the frighteners on Rob. Wandsworth was full of violent prisoners who'd intimidate for payment or a favour, and Delfont had the underworld contacts to arrange a warm welcome. It would have been a different matter coming after a serving DI and her daughter. In the end, all the incidents that had so terrified Shona had been the work of James McGowan's stalker, Bryson Drake – born Joseph Bishop in Falmouth – a man who'd lived many lives. He'd been the one who'd grabbed Becca in the garden and sent the three bullets that Shona had believed were for her family. Her friend Professor Sue Kitchen had tried to alert her – *have you considered you may also be experiencing hyper-vigilance yourself?* – but Shona had brushed it aside, and it had almost cost James McGowan his life. If she'd really listened to the fans, understood how the extra on set was using their encyclopaedic knowledge of James to plan his attacks, and if she'd seen Brian Ashton as something other than a sexual predator – another Delfont in the making – then maybe she'd have stopped James's stalker sooner.

Delfont had wanted his victims to think he could get to them anywhere and Shona had been convinced it was true. Thalia had also believed in the threat, and that had been why it backfired on him so spectacularly. He'd pushed Thalia Brookes into a living hell where she could only see one way out: killing her attacker.

To her surprise, Shona found she could not condemn Thalia for what she'd done. Perhaps, like Robert Burns, Shona had come to understand the struggle between official justice and natural justice, and would, in time, need to make the necessary accommodation with events she could not change.

–

On Kirkness beach, she watched Becca load her pockets with her chosen pebbles. *I let someone get away with murder for you*, Shona thought. *I can't ever tell you. I can't tell anyone, but I did it for you.*

Perhaps her daughter, mentally at least, was already on her way to university in Glasgow and to archaeology digs in the deserts of Egypt, Syria or Iraq, armed with Ric and Ben's survival skills, already enjoying a life free from Delfont's shadow. Shona could live with that. Maybe Becca would carry a little bit of Kirkness in her pocket and come home to her old mum, now and again. If Shona was still here. Rob had had to face the consequences of his actions. One day Shona might face the same.

When Rob called now, he spent the bulk of his allotted time talking to Becca. With Delfont dead, he'd agreed to go ahead with the appeal, but he was no longer keen to talk to Shona about the details, and that was fine by her.

Slasher Sue had been right all along. Michael Vincent's death was most likely accidental. The Zodiac RIB hadn't been found. It was possible it had, as Tommy suggested, been sold on or wrecked and dragged out to deep water by the tide. Matt from the security company was now in the custody of Kent Police, being questioned in relation to drug offences. It seemed likely he'd been the one supplying Vincent and had perhaps even seen him fall, and then loosened the boat to make it look like the actor had left the island and acquired his drugs elsewhere. Kent Police might ask him just such a question, but it was unlikely they'd ever know the truth. The mystery would be revisited in documentaries and podcasts perpetuating Vincent's fame beyond his death, and perhaps that's the way he would have wanted it.

Fuelled by the sympathetic publicity following James's shooting and the tragedies on set, the film was already being talked up as a commercial hit.

Shona had taken to visiting James each morning, waved in by the nurses who made no enquiry about her reasons. He was still pale, and Shona found it difficult to look at the stapled wound above his left ear, but he seemed a little stronger with every passing day. He was due to be transferred to a hospital in Glasgow.

'It's all my aunties' and cousins' doin',' he'd said. 'Just so they can come an' make a fuss of me. Will you come too?'

'Will your aunties let me in?'

He'd made a dubious face. 'Probably harder than getting past Ric and Ben. But soon as they know you're fae the scheme, ye'll be fine.'

Then he'd become serious. 'Would High Pines be interested in a partnership?'

'How d'you mean?'

'I'm looking tae invest in Scotland, and Lilly's right. *It's the cutest B&B.*' He mimicked her accent to perfection, and it made Shona smile. 'In fact,' James went on, 'Lilly was thinking of puttin' in an offer, but I threatened to keep hold of her bodyguards. Plus, she didn't think you'd sell.'

'She's right. We can't afford to sell.'

'What about a one-third share for £250K? Clear your debts. Help reposition the business?'

It was on the tip of her tongue to say that sounded like a lot of cash for a single night of passion, but she knew it wasn't what he meant. The offer wasn't motivated by guilt. It wasn't a pay-off.

He'd said she'd grown into herself. He had too. They were different people since that high-school kiss, yet somehow the same. The shared upbringing among poverty and despair was written through them. She would take him up on his investment offer. There wasn't anyone she trusted more than James right now.

Rob would have little say in the matter. His appeal might not be successful. It would take five years to be eligible for parole. No one could change the past, but the past just might change her future. She needed to do what was best for her and Becca now.

Becca came crunching across the shingle to her mother, clutching a pebble.

'Look, Mum, it's shaped like a heart.' She placed the scarlet stone in her mother's hand. A heart of fire, forged in the Solway. 'What's going to happen with Dad?'

'There's enough evidence for an appeal, I think,' Shona said.

'No, I mean with you and Dad? You're not wearing your ring anymore, and on the beach, when James was shot, you called him *Jaz* and *my love*. Does that mean you *do* love him? D'you love him more than Dad?'

Shona pulled her close. 'Oh, darlin'. You are my number one priority.'

'I know. But I'll be off to university soon. I'm a big girl,' she said into her mother's hair.

'You are not,' Shona squeezed. 'You're ma wee girl and always will be.'

Becca stepped back, out of her embrace, and gave her mother a look that seemed wise beyond her years. 'Lots of parents live apart. You'll still be my mum and dad. I just want you to be happy. Do what you need to do, Mum, to be happy.'

Becca touched the stone in her mother's hand. 'You should give it to James, from all of us, so he doesn't forget to come back.'

Her old friend had obviously made a favourable impression on Becca. Maybe her daughter was fed up with the troubled nature of her parents' marriage. Or, as an only child, she welcomed the idea of a new, blended family that would bring her siblings. Dove and Beau, perhaps?

Shona had thought it over. She knew James's life was in America, with his children, his work and friends like Lilly Chase. Shona's place was here. But their connection had been re-established. Maybe it had never really been broken, just buried, and who knew what the future might bring. Her fingers closed around the pebble, and she slipped it into her pocket.

Shona saw the storm approaching fast on a wind that drew tears from her eyes. The colours dimmed and the air thickened, but she knew it would pass. Would the birds return? It might take a while for them to regain their former strength, but the shores and marshes would hear their calls once more and they'd raise their families here, she was sure of it.

Shona had her family too; it had just taken her a while to realise it. Becca, Murdo, Ravi, Kate, Dan, Tommy, Freya and James. Not by blood or legal ceremony, but family all the same.

Acknowledgements

Thank you to my wonderful editors at Canelo, Louise Cullen and Katy Loftus, who saw merit in this idea, and Alicia Pountney, whose steady hand guided it to completion. Thank you also to my brilliant developmental editor Russel D McLean, copy editor Daniela Nava and eagle-eyed proofreader Becca Allen, and the sales and marketing team who endeavour to get the right books into the hands of the right readers. A special thank you to my agent, Anne Williams at KHLA, for wise words and bringing her vast experience to bear on the manuscript.

Though Robert Burns was born in neighbouring Ayrshire, he lived most of his adult life in Dumfries and Galloway, and you can't visit the area without noticing how closely he is held in hearts there. It was a desire to reflect this, and perhaps purge the horror of enforced classroom recitation felt by many a Scottish school pupil, that led me to look at him again. His output as a writer was prodigious – more than 550 poems and songs – and many more letters and articles. His work is marked by a complex and modern voice, preoccupied with many of our contemporary concerns – including social justice and the environment – which also prove challenging for DI Shona Oliver.

I'm indebted to the Robert Burns House for sight of some original manuscripts and Burns's personal belongings. A huge thank you to Joyce and Ian Cochrane of Old Bank Books in Wigtown, who not only provided me with invaluable texts, but also a bed for the night in their bookshop, which was once the town's Custom House, and was undoubtably visited by Robert Burns himself, back in the day. I'm sure he'd prefer the building's modern incarnation, and like myself, wish you every success in the future.

The RNLI station at Kippford were once again generous in offering insightful details about their life-saving and inspiring work. My thanks also to Mersehead Nature Reserve and the RSPB for the sometimes–heart-breaking statistics on bird flu and bird migration.

Thank you to my former Crime Writing MA cohort at the University of East Anglia, who continue to be a huge source of support, and to tutor Tom Benn, whose screenwriting insights proved invaluable in creating this book.

My eternal gratitude goes to Sarah Barnes of Hijinx theatre company for her continued friendship, support, and explanations of acting and film processes. Also, to Charles Simpson, fountain of extraordinary knowledge (antique weapons, on this occasion!) and fiendish plot-knot un-tangler. Any errors are, of course, mine alone.

Finally, a special thank you to my home team – Mickey, Leo, Chloe, Sam and Thomas – who often live with my characters as much as I do.

Writing can sometimes feel like a solitary business, but really, we exist within a fantastic community of book-shops, readers groups and book festivals. To those who maintain these beacons of light in difficult times and in the face of innumerable obstacles, I send you my heartfelt thanks.

Do you love crime fiction and are always on the lookout for brilliant authors?

Canelo Crime is home to some of the most exciting novels around. Thousands of readers are already enjoying our compulsive stories. Are you ready to find your new favourite writer?

Find out more and sign up to our newsletter at canelocrime.com